As I See Sex
Through the Bible

BY

ROBERT L. PETTUS, JR., M.D.

Robert L. Pettus, Jr., M.D.
114 Madison Street
Madison, Tennessee 37115

Copyright 1973 by
Robert L. Pettus, Jr., M.D.

PRINTED BY WILLIAMS ● NASHVILLE

Dedication

To my wife NITA, the love of my life, the mother of my children and my source of strength, comfort and encouragement.

Unless otherwise noted all quotations from the Scriptures are from the King James Version. RSV stands for Revised Standard Version and ASV is for the American Standard Version.

Acknowledgments

ALL THAT I AM I owe to someone. I am indebted to my parents, my teachers, my wife and c h i l d r e n, the Madison Church and its elders and ministers, and my patients who trust me with their lives. Without the encouragement of many of these, I would not have attempted to get these lessons into print.

I am indebted to Mrs. Marie Pilkinton for typing these lessons from my longhand manuscript. To Mrs. Nila Sherrill I am indebted for advice and for proofreading my efforts.

Table of Contents

Preface 7
1. Scope of Study 9
2. Teaching Children 17
3. Advice to Teenagers 26
4. The Dangers of Going Steady 30
5. Harlots, Whores, and Prostitutes 38
6. Marriage 40
7. The Husband and the Home 48
8. The Wife and the Home 62
9. Dyspareunia and Vaginismus 71
10. Pre-Marital and Extra-Marital Relations 75
11. The Menopause and the Christian Home 78
12. The Male Climacteric 89
13. Sexual Perversions 94
14. Masturbation 102
15. Birth Control and the Bible 105
16. Birth Control—Why and How 110
17. Mandrakes 122
18. Circumcision 125
19. Venereal Disease 128
20. Eunuchs 133
21. Abortions 137
22. Oral Genital Sex 142
Conclusion 145

Preface

THIS BOOK is the outgrowth of a series of lessons that I gave first to my Sunday Morning Bible Class at the Madison Church of Christ. The lessons were so well received I was asked to give them again on Wednesday nights. The attendance at the Wednesday classes ranged close to 500 from teenagers through all ages. These lessons were taped and from these tapes came these edited and organized chapters.

The reader should realize that by profession I am a physician. I do a family type of general practice in Madison, Tennessee, a suburb of Nashville.

The thoughts of these lessons are mine and even though they were delivered at the Madison Church they are not necessarily endorsed by the leaders of the Madison Church. These lessons are not entirely the results of my experiences but are the results of my studies, extensive readings and the insight I have gained from counseling with my patients for the past twenty-three years.

ROBERT L. PETTUS, JR., M.D.

CHAPTER 1

Scope of Study

I AM SPEAKING from over forty-five years of Bible study, from over twenty years of medical practice and from counseling patients with problems, personal, sexual and medical. I speak also from twenty-two years of happy married life. Some of the things of which I speak come from one area and some from another. These certainly are not all personal experiences. I have derived my thoughts from many different sources.

I will mention patients I have seen over a period of twenty years. These patients could be from Madison, Oak Ridge, Orlinda or Memphis, Tennessee. There is no way for you to know the identity of anyone I might mention. I will use examples to illustrate points in our discussion.

It might be of interest, before we get too far along, to tell you about some of the things I will be discussing.

Is it scriptural to have lessons on sex, or as I have termed it, Christian Sex Education?

Is it right? Is it Biblical?

If it is not, let us stop now.

I want to talk about man's basic desires or drives as the psychologist calls them. I want to talk about our children and their rights, about sex and marriage, about the dangers of going steady, about the things to tell your children and how to advise them.

I want to talk about the role of the husband in the home, some of his duties as a mate, some of the things that the husband should do in foreplay and other suggestions along this line. I want to talk about some of the things that suppress the sexual drive in males and some of the forms of male impotency. I want to discuss prostatism. I want to talk about the wife, the home, the wife's duties, as well as some basic differences between males and females, between men and women.

I will speak about the five ways we are sexually stimulated and give Bible references where each of these was recognized by the writers of the Old Testament.

I will talk about premarital and extramarital sex. The newspapers speak of these; but I will talk about them in their true sense, fornication and adultery, as the Bible speaks of them. I will speak on dyspareunia and vaginismus and explain these terms.

I will talk about the menopause and its effects on the Christian home. How it affects the woman going through this period of her life, how it affects the husband, what the children should know about it, and how to treat the menopausal woman will also be included in the discussion. Some of the methods available to her for the amelioration of her symptoms will be mentioned.

I want to discuss the male climacteric which is the analogous syndrome in the male.

I will talk about the Bible teachings concerning birth control. I will speak about sexual perversions.

I intend to quote scriptures along with the lessons we are studying. I believe there are scriptures which teach or illustrate every one of these basic areas mentioned for discussion. Since they are taught and discussed in the Bible, I think it is right for us to bring them up here and to explain in language that all can understand. Let us see how we can profit from a study of each.

To reiterate my belief that this study is scriptural and Biblical, let us look at the following scriptures. Remember in Genesis 1:27: "So God created man in His own image, in the image of God created He him; male and female created He them." Here we find in the first chapter of Genesis the writer is talking about males and females. Really this is the name of the game. Males and females are what the whole study is about. Genesis 5:2 says, "Male and female created he them." Six times in Genesis man is told to be "fruitful and multiply" (Genesis 1:22, 28; 8:17, 9:1,7; 35:11). He is told to "replenish the earth." This is not possible without sexual relations. From this we know that married couples are commanded to have sexual relations.

I want to point out that all sexual relations must be within the relationship of marriage. Any sexual relationship outside of marriage is sinful. It is condemned. It is not to be practiced. It is not to be condoned.

10

Since a relationship like this is ordained of God, ordered by Him, blessed by Him, I think it is right for us to talk about it.

I will talk about some of the wider ramifications of sex and marriage. I want to tell of some of the ways sex is used wrongly by husbands and wives. Sometimes sex is denied as punishment for behavior, for purchases, for family black mail and various other reasons. I will talk about false teachings concerning sex. I will talk about some false practices.

Since we have found that it is right and proper for us to teach these lessons, the next question arises.

Is there a real need for teaching along this line? I think this question is answered in the affirmative by the five hundred plus present to hear this lesson. The Church does not have a good teaching program on the subject. There has been virtually no teaching on sex in the Church. If you go to buy a book written by a member of the Lord's Church along this line, there is not one good complete authoritative book available. Those available go no deeper than what you would expect from a high school student.

We have the same nature, the same drives, the same inhibitions, the same temptations and the same needs as they did in Biblical times. They were given instructions on how to act, what to do, what was right, what was wrong and what was perversion. Because of these reasons, I believe we need to be taught so that we will know how to behave ourselves, as well as what to teach our children and our grandchildren. We need to know how to talk with each other. I do not think it is wrong to talk about sex as long as your reason for discussing it is worthwhile.

There has been much written in the newspapers lately about sex and the Bible. You may have read articles that quoted the Bible stating that certain scriptures were pornographic. Some have compared the Bible with pornography.

The difference between pornography and the quoted Bible stories is that pornography is written to stimulate sensual drives and sensualism; whereas, the Bible records incidents to tell us what is right and what is wrong. The Bible was not designed to create an abnormal sensual drive in the person or individual.

As parents, we need to know what to teach our children. I think this is the reason many of you are here.

"What should I teach my child?" is often asked. We will have an entire lesson on what to teach the one-year-olds, the two-year-olds and on up to the teen-ager.

Husbands need to know how to fulfill their obligations to their wives. They need to know how to treat them—what to do to them and for them. Wives need to know how to fulfill their obligations of marriage to their husbands. These are commandments found in I Corinthians 7. Husbands and wives are commanded not to refrain from having relations. This will be discussed in detail later.

Young couples need to know how to fulfill their obligations and how to enjoy the privileges of marriage. There are many privileges in marriage, but also there are many obligations. Sex in marriage is both a privilege and an obligation. We are commanded to have sexual relations. We are commanded not to refrain from them. If sexual relations were only an obligation, sex would not be fun. One of the reasons sex is fun is that it is a privilege. I want to have a lesson on the teachings of Solomon concerning the enjoyment he received. Certainly we have the same drives and the same instincts he had.

I want to discuss some of the changing attitudes toward sex in America today. As most of you know, we are having what many call a sexual revolution in America today. The so-called new morality has a great number of people looking at things differently. One of the reason is the change in names. Instead of speaking of adultery and fornication it is referred to as extra-marital and pre-marital sex. When the name is changed, the sin does not seem as black. This is only one of the problems. Other problems include the following: there is more pre-marital promiscuity; there is also more open sexual perversion practiced today than was the case twenty years ago.

Perversion has become quite a problem in Nashville. Many of you may remember the raids carried out by the police in our local Centennial Park just a few years ago. This was a well known hangout for male homosexuals. (Remember I am still talking about why we should talk about sex in the church.) You may be surprised to know that the largest number of male homosexuals that the police picked up in Centennial Park were teachers and preachers. Preachers in Churches of Christ were the second most numerous mentioned. They were close behind the number who preached for the largest denomination in our city. This I think is deplorable. If you answer that they constitute a minority, I agree. However, if one gospel preacher or one Bible school teacher is a homosexual, it is a problem. It is a problem because homosexualism is condemned in the Bible. I think there is a need for lots of teaching along these lines.

From my own experience I have found a change in the complaints of members of the church from what they were twenty years ago. Twenty years ago it was quite common to have men complain to me about their cold, frigid, indifferent wives. They would describe how distant they were and how they would resist having sexual relations. This is still a common complaint, but twenty years ago I never had a complaint of a woman about an indifferent husband. Yet with the change in times, the change in morality, the change in dress and the change in whatever influences my patients have, I now find a great number of women with husbands who will not have relations with them regularly or who ignore them entirely.

You say I am speaking in generalities and this I am. However, I can tell you of a patient, a woman, married for three years with one child. Her chief complaint for which she consulted me was that she could not stay awake long enough or wait long enough for her husband to have sexual relations with her. He either stayed out with the boys; or, if he did come home, he would sit up to play with and make plastic cars. This is abnormal behavior to me and it provokes you to laughter. This is not an isolated case. I have heard this and similar stories frequently.

Next, I think of a woman who was raised in a sister congregation near here. She married her high school sweetheart with whom she had worshiped at the same congregation all her life. After being married two years she divorced him. I asked her why? She said, "Dr. Pettus, after about two weeks he never came to bed with me. He was always out with the boys." Think of this. After about two weeks of married life, no sexual relations despite an anxious warm desiring wife. I think the woman was cheated. We need to teach our boys that if they marry they are expected to have sexual relations with their wives, that they are expected to live with their wives as a husband. And, if

13

they do not intend to do this, we should teach them not to marry and mess up a girl's life. This is not something that happens only occasionally or among the uneducated.

I remember counseling with the wife of a preacher who had been married for a number of years. This woman was married to a man who had refused to have relations with her and refused to seek professional help for his problem. She had a normal God-given sex drive with no outlet even though she slept nightly in the same bed with her husband. You may ask why she married him. I asked her this. Her answer was, "I thought he was a good boy. He was studying to preach. I appreciated him not pawing and trying to handle me before we were married." What kind of a counselor for couples with sexual problems can this man be?

I want to discuss this further in the lesson we will have on what to teach our children, but now let me give this advice. Tell your daughters to be aware of the boy who is so perfect he does not test her defenses. Be sure you advise her to keep her defenses. There is a need for this type of teaching and study.

There is a need for sex education because of the enormous proportions to which venereal disease has risen. Billboards proclaim this as our number one contagious disease after the common cold. It passes measles, whooping cough and chicken pox.

It is disturbing to talk to a member of the church who is married to a member of the church and find that he has contracted a venereal disease from his wife who has been promiscuous, having adulterous relations, while he has been earning a living.

The question comes up. Where did the sex drive originate? The Lord put it in us. We each have certain basic forces within ourselves which the psychologist calls drives. We recognize that we have these drives and know that they either have to be satisfied or sublimated. If this drive is not satisfied, it must be sublimated. One must keep pushing it back and not let it come to the forefront.

Women have a maternal drive, that is the drive or desire to have a baby. In some women this is quite pronounced. They want to mother a child or mother others. This drive can be sublimated. If a woman is not married, or if married and has no child, she can find something else to occupy her mind. She can keep busy.

The hunger drive present in all of us has to be satisfied. True, it can be sublimated for a short time. After about forty days of fasting, most will die.

The thirst drive is a strong drive that can be sublimated only about three days.

Some of us believe there is a worship drive. Many psychologists deny that this is a drive. I think it is, but I think it is one of our weaker drives. It is not a strong drive. It is easy to sublimate. One can do most anything to suppress this drive, wander from the Church or keep from worshiping the Lord.

The sex drive is within every individual. It has to be cultivated in some individuals at certain times. It also has to be controlled. The very fact that the Lord put it in us and we are commanded to control it lets us know that it is indeed possible to control or sublimate our sex drive. It is a command that we control it until after marriage. I think this also implies that prior to marriage our sex drive can and must be controlled. We also must recognize the sex drive is stronger in some individuals than in others. This influences life even in the birth to five year old age group. The sex drive is in the child even at this young age. It's manifested in children at this age. I have seen motion pictures made by psychologists of children in cribs moving, turning and twisting to stimulate their genitals to derive some infantile satisfaction.

It is told that French nurses by placing their hand on and by stimulating the genitals of infants are able to quickly quiet them. This is one way the sex drive is stimulated. Children learn this themselves by accidental self-stimulation.

A drive must be satisfied or sublimated. The sex drive must be sublimated until after marriage. I also want to point out that adultery is a sin and always has been a sin. It does not matter how many talk about morality or the new morality. This will not change the basic teaching of the Bible. There cannot be full satisfaction of the sex drive outside of marriage for this is a sin.

Jesus in the Sermon on the Mount taught a lesson on Christian sex education. Remember in Matthew 5:27-28 he said, "Ye have heard that it was said by them of old times, Thou shalt not commit adultery: But I say unto you, That whosoever looketh on a woman to lust after her hath committed adultery with her already in his heart." Christ spoke about this. We should want to learn as much as we can about the sex drive.

Some questions come to mind. Can the single person control his or her sex drive? Can the married control their sex drive? Do we have to submit to our impulses and to our temptations and have extra-marital or adulterous relations? In the unmarried is this drive so strong it cannot be controlled? I do not think it is. Paul in I Corinthians 10:13 wrote, "God is faithful, who will not suffer you to be tempted above that ye are able; but will with the temptation also make a way to escape, that ye may be able to bear it." Remember this when you are tempted to yield to temptation.

More often we speak of men lusting after women. Certainly women lust after men also. This depends on the situation, the strength of the drive, and how strong the individual resists temptation, that is, how much attempt is being made to sublimate the sex drive.

Satisfaction of the sex drive in the marriage relationship is right, is expected and is demanded. The scriptures, Genesis 1:28, Genesis 3:16, Exodus 21:10 and I Corinthians 7:2-5, verify this.

CHAPTER 2

Teaching Children

I WANT TO re-establish that it is Biblical and it is right to teach lessons on sex. I think this was obvious with some of the passages that we read last week. The many passages in Genesis concerning being fruitful and replenishing the earth prove this.

We also established that there is a need for this type of lesson. Parents, physicians, preachers, teachers, and social workers know there is a need for sex instruction to our children.

I want to talk about children and their rights. We have privileges as parents and we have obligations as parents. Children have certain rights.

I think children deserve to be wanted. If you have a child and the child knows that he is not wanted, then this child is going to have a difficult time making adjustments in later life; making adjustments to his partner and making adjustments to the world.

Children deserve to be loved. As parents, we are commanded in Titus 2:4 to love our children. There are other passages in the Bible that show we are to love our children, love our wives and love our husbands. We certainly are supposed to love our children.

I think every child should have a chance to grow as Jesus did. "And Jesus increased in wisdom and stature, and in favor with God and man" (Luke 2:52). Jesus increased mentally, physically, religiously and socially. These are the four areas that we all need to grow in. As our study goes along, we will find some of the areas and ways to improve the way they develop and grow.

I think also a child deserves to be born into a Christian home. Some may disagree but any of you who are here, who are married to non-Christians, can see the wisdom of having both parents Christians.

Contrast the home of a child where neither parent is a Christian with the home of a child where the mother and father are united in their attitudes toward God and in their dedication

17

towards living a Christian life before the child and in bringing up this child as a Christian.

If a child has the right to be born into a Christian home, a child should have the right to be reared in a Christian home.

I think another thing that a child deserves is the right to be taught the truth. "For what is a man profited, if he shall gain the whole world, and lose his own soul? or what shall a man give in exchange for his soul?" (Matthew 16:26).

No matter how much we work, strive and sacrifice to give our children material things, if we do not put in them the love of God, if we do not teach them what Christ would have them know concerning Him, how then can they have a hope of salvation?

If we do not give our child the hope of eternal life, we have slighted our child. We all know the passage that says, "Train up a child in the way he should go and when he is old he will not depart from it" (Proverbs 22:6). We have all heard this all of our lives. How many of you have heard Proverbs 29:15, "A child left to himself bringeth his mother to shame."

Many parents have truly had shame brought upon them because their children were ignorant of sex education. Parents who give no instruction, but rather let their children grow up learning about sex from the back alley, are asking for trouble. Many times parents avoid teaching by saying that sex education is not necessary. Children grow up then lacking the correct information about sex and eventually bring shame and heartache to parents.

The Bible deals with the subject of sex. We read a passage last week where Christ in the Sermon on the Mount talked about adultery and a man looking on a woman and lusting after her. This was a sex lesson in the Sermon on the Mount.

Some will say, I do not want my child to learn too young. I would like to know how young is too young? Last year in the Metropolitan Nashville School System among girls between the ages of twelve and sixteen there were 150 known pregnancies.[1] Add to that the number that was not known and the number who were pregnant and spontaneously aborted. This is in the

---

[1] Personal communication from a counselor in the Metropolitan Nashville School System.

sixteen year olds and under. It does not count those seventeen years and older, where the incidence of courting and going steady is higher. Many of these girls are having anovulatory periods, which means that these girls are having menstrual cycles in which they are not shedding an egg and cannot become pregnant.

The incidences of promiscuity are great. Therefore, I do not think you can teach a child too young.

Sixteen years old is tenth grade and under. Let's talk about something closer to home. Let us come back to the Madison congregation and talk about something that has happened since I have been attending here.

In a sixth grade prayer meeting class a group of four girls were caught copying a pornographic letter describing in great detail a hot date. They were spending prayer meeting time copying a letter purporting to be a letter written from one girl to another about a hot date. She had described everything from a car ride, to kissing, to the heavy petting, to the unclothing, to the pain, to the ecstasy and the finish. This was here at Madison. Our children will learn about sex whether we want them to learn or not. It may be by experimentation, or they may learn from someone who does not know how to teach them. Let us try to do the very best job we can do. I think even at best we are going to make a lot of mistakes.

To do the best job possible we must prepare ourselves. One thing we must remember when we are teaching children is that a small child does not put the same connotation on words as we do. They have to be taught that certain things are not to be discussed in certain places. You have to teach a child that it is wrong to talk about bowel movements in public. You have to teach them to wear clothes. A three-year-old does not worry if he walks out in the yard with no clothes or goes to the door with no clothes. We teach them certain things and part of our obligation as parents is to teach them this. When teaching children, remember you must give fast answers. You cannot hem and haw around and say I will think about this and answer you tomorrow. You must answer them right away. Sometimes you have to be on the defensive. You have to have an answer ahead of time. By all means you must give an honest answer.

If a child asks, "Where did I come from?" and you tell him

19

the stork brought him, you have lied to the child. When the child asks another question and you answer with a lie or a silly answer, the child will know very soon that he will not get the correct answer at home. He will say to himself, I may as well find out from someone else. Therefore, we must give fast answers, honest answers and suitable answers in a language the child can understand. I think it does no good to talk over a person's head. Physicians are frequently accused of using language the patients to whom they are speaking do not understand. It is better to say fifteen words the patient understands than to spend twenty minutes talking in a language the patient has no idea about what you are speaking. Remember Paul in I Corinthians 14:19 spoke of the uselessness in speaking in an unknown tongue. I think this applies to the age group we are now discussing.

An example[2] is the six year old who at the supermarket picks up a box of sanitary napkins and asks his mother, "What are these?" Tell him it is a box of sanitary napkins. He may know it already from the television advertisement. When he asks, "What are they for?: The best thing to tell him is that they are something grown women use. This will usually satisfy a child and you will rarely have to go into detail, but if he asks more questions, answer him truthfully. Perhaps the next question will be, "Where are the cookies?" or "Will you buy me a coke?" He will not continue the questioning and have you give in full detail when they use them, how they are used or why they use them. At least you have been honest with him. When he learns something else along this line, he will know you have been candid with him. He will have something honest with which to attach new information rather than some story you have concocted.

A baby has a very small pelvis, and a big pot belly. He can hardly see his privates, but when he gets two or three years old, his pelvis gets bigger and the stomach gets smaller because it drops down into his pelvis. The child is running around more and is losing weight. Sometimes about this age, when the stomach is getting flatter, little boys discover that they have a penis. When it starts itching, he scratches it. The first thing some mothers think is that they have an oversexed child or that

---

[2] *The Children's Doctor*, Linden Smith, M.D., Chapter 9.

something is really wrong with him because he is playing with himself. A good way of handling this instead of smacking him down right off, is to ask him if his penis is itching. He may be a little embarrassed when he answers yes, but rather than make a big to do about it, you can come up with a good answer and say it is the bubble bath or perhaps that something has bitten him or some other plausible answer. Then he gets the idea that this is something that is not dirty. You may suggest that boys do not scratch themselves in public. It is better to say nothing than to make a big to do over it.

You know one thing a woman cannot hide is being pregnant. If you have a three-year-old, he knows that something is wrong with his mother, that something is happening when she is about seven months pregnant. He may ask, "Why are you so fat?" You know, I have heard them say, I swallowed a pumpkin seed, which is far fetched. How many have heard this? I think a much better answer would be is that your brother or sister is growing inside your mother. Tell them that in a couple of months that it will be large enough to grow on the outside. A child does not attach a whole lot of significance to these things but at least you are planting little truths in his mind and not misconceptions. Maybe the next question will be, "Can I have a baby?" This gives you a chance to do a little talking. You can say not yet, you will have to wait until you are grown and married, because single people do not have babies. Instead of stopping here you can tell a three-year-old when the baby comes that it will be his or her baby whichever the case, and that he can help mother take care of it. You can go further and say, if you like being a mama, when you are grown and married, you can have your own child. I think this is a much healthier way than to make up a lot of concoctions of pumpkin seed and things like that. I never could fathom this.

One other thing that comes up many times when children are between four and six years old is that frequently a mother will get a call from the neighborhood troublemaker. She will call the mother of a four-year-old boy and say, "I caught your four-year-old boy looking at my four-year-old girl's privates." She is screaming, hollering and talking about nasty, dirty boys. She asks why you raised one like this, or what is he going to do, rape her? She will start talking about calling the police and have him taken in. She suggests that the child needs a psychiatrist. She will announce if you do not get things straightened out she will move from the neighborhood. The first reaction of most mothers is that the four-year-old girl must be a flirt and will probably end up later a prostitute anyway. Probably the very best way to handle this is to be real cool about the whole thing and promise you will talk to your son about the situation. Tell her you will have your husband talk to him, and if she wants you to that you will talk to your family physician or pediatrician. This will calm her down. At least once a year I get a call about this. Do not get too upset with the woman that calls to tell you about your four-year-old, she is just misinterpreting what he is doing and there is no point in getting up tight about this. Do not get upset with your boy for putting you in such an embarrassing situation and by all means do not get upset with yourself for not watching him so close that he could not do this. You just cannot watch a four-year-old every minute, if you could, you certainly would not want to. It would drive you crazy trying to keep after him. There are certain things that you do not want; one of these is to constantly be saying no, no, no. You must let them learn some things for themselves, but just be calm and promise her you will talk to him. When he comes in he will probably have mixed emotions. The woman probably has already chewed him out, fussed at him and called him several bad names; and he does not know to be scared. He comes in puzzled and you ask him what happened. He will probably tell you, "We were playing doctors," or something of that nature. You ask him if the little girl was sick and he may answer, "No, we were just checking." You ask if he was trying to find out if she was a boy or girl and ask if that is why you looked at her and he will probably say, "Yes." Then this is a good chance for you to tell him the difference between boys and girls. If he has or does not have a sister, this is a good opportunity to teach a lesson. Tell him that girls have a vagina. I think that it is good to pronounce a word the right way and va-ji'-na is the right pronunciation. It is a little disturbing to talk with girls who come in for pre-marital talks and things of this nature when they do not know what to call various organs of the body. You can explain to the child that it is the same the world over. Little boys are made one way and little girls another, and this is the way the Lord made them. Certainly, there is nothing to be ashamed of. Perhaps you can draw some pictures about the vagina, if he does not understand. You may also tell him that a part of the doctor's job is to check various parts of the body, and then suggest to him that mothers of little girls do not want their little girls checked on or inspected by anyone else. Try to present it in such a way that he will not think it is dirty, but that it is just not done at that time. Tell him if he wants more information, come and ask you. You can tell him that if you do not know the answer you will get a book and look it up. This is usually enough to satisfy a child of this age.

Sometimes you get a six-year-old who does not ask questions. It is difficult to know whether they know more than what they are asking or if they are not being inquisitive. Often this is because of the talk of the parents. Some parents never speak about matters concerning sex, relationships, pregnancies or babies. This whole realm in some households is different, especially at my house with the phone and the various things that I have to ask people on the phone. We did not have this problem but certainly some six-year-olds have never asked about the parts of the body and the differences in sexes or how life begins.

You might if you have a child like this ask her, "Mary, I'm curious, do you know where babies come from?" She probably will say, "Yes, out of mama's belly." You might ask, "Do you know how they get out?" This would be a good time to teach her about birth and about the delivery. One child reported to the mother that babies came out through the belly button. The mother said that this is not quite true and she had the opportunity to tell her little girl that the baby comes out the vagina and this is the front opening of her bottom. Girls can relate these things when you say the front opening of the bottom. Then at least she knows where it is and knows she has one. The little girl who reported that babies came from the belly button was asked by her mother, "Who told you it was the belly button?" She said, "Joe; he is a smart boy; he knows everything. His father is a dentist."

This would be a good time to tell your child that we learn by asking questions and tell him that you know some things that Joe does not know and if you do not know the answer you

23

do know where to go to look it up. We do not have to rely on Joe because here we found out that there are some things that Joe does not know. This has taken about four of five minutes which is about the time span that you can hold this age child's interest. They are ready to drop the subject and go on to something else and maybe this is a good time to stop asking questions and let them wait awhile. Maybe a year, six months or three months later come back to the same subject and ask them if they know how the baby gets into the mama's stomach? They can watch Jaques Cousteau, the French biologist who has all the underwater pictures on television about the fertilization of fish eggs and mammals and learn most of the reproductive process. This would be a good time to find out from the child if he knows how the baby gets in the inside of mama's stomach. A six-year-old may report that mama swallowed it. This would be a good time to tell him, "No, she did not, but daddy planted a seed in the vagina and the seed met the egg that was formed by mother. The egg was there already. With the union of the seed and egg, the baby begins to grow. You might suggest that after awhile when the baby is large enough that it comes to the outside through the vagina. You can also say every baby and every person in the world began like this. It developed inside the mother and was born. This is truth and is no more difficult to understand than the pumpkin seed story, and obviously it is worth a whole lot more to the child. Certainly this is in keeping with training up a child right, then you do not have to undo any learning. If you learn a lot of wrong things, you must of necessity unlearn these as you acquire and assimilate the right things. You do not want to push a subject, but wait till a child is ready.

I think one thing for sure girls should know about is the menstrual cycle before it is time for her periods to begin. It is terrorizing for a girl to awake or to be sitting in school and find that she has blood in her panties. If she is not given correct information, she may have preconceived ideas that stem from hearing things that are wrong. Then she will equate the menstrual cycle oftentime with fear, with shame, and with pain and she may have problems throughout life and the entire menstrual cycle. A great amount of menstrual pain is emotional or psychological and I think that every girl should be taught

24

right. They are doing some great jobs in our public schools. Sometimes it is a little late and some of you do not want your child to learn at school. This seems to me to be one thing that every mother can teach her own daughter. Every woman has gone through it, but do not wait too long to tell your little girl. Do not think that your little girl is going to wait till she is fifteen to begin. Teach her the function of the menstrual cycle. There are many books written that anyone can understand. They can be obtained from your physician. Every sanitary napkin company offers books that you can send off for for your child. By all means you should emphasize that the menstrual cycle is normal and anything that is normal you need to know about. I do not mind talking about this before men because a great number of men have a hang-up about the menstrual cycle or are confused about it. I am afraid some even marry before they know that the menstrual cycle is normal. Let us try not to push it too much or too hard or go into great details at one time.

Next week, I want to begin a study on going steady. I think this is a problem that all of us who have children have or will have and must face up to. Any of you who have grandchildren are going to be faced with it and even if you do not have children or grandchildren there may be a time that some teenager will come to you and ask you about this as a Bible School teacher. You may be the confidant of some child. We should know some of the reasons for not going steady.

CHAPTER 3

Advice to Teenagers

THERE ARE some things that teenagers should know. There are some things that parents should teach their children. Parents should teach their children defensive courting as drivers are taught defensive driving. In driving this means anticipating the other driver's actions and responses before he makes them. It means having your car under control no matter what the other driver does. It means planning ahead, seeing the dangers and avoiding the dangers. If the road is slick, it means slowing down. If there is a turn, decreasing the speed. All of these indicate being in control of the automobile.

Defensive courting and defensive living is the same. Look ahead, see where the dangers are and avoid them. Build your defenses and avoid sin. Avoid the wrong company. The RSV says, "Evil companions corrupt good morals" (I Corinthians 15:33). In Psalms 1:1 David said, "Blessed is the man that walketh not in the counsel of the ungodly, nor standeth in the way of sinners, nor sitteth in the seat of the scornful."

Secondly, to court defensively avoid being alone where there is opportunity and temptation to yield to temptation. Children should not be left alone at home. Teenagers should not be alone in their homes.

A fellow general practitioner, Dr. James Hastie, with whom I sometimes share coverage has told me he is not surprised at the large number of non-virgin teenagers since so many of them are left alone in their homes by their parents. I agree with him.

The drive-in movie is another place where there is a great temptation. To be alone in close contact sitting and watching a sensuous movie for two to four hours is great temptation. The defensive courter will avoid these.

The parked car is a great potential danger. If you park to talk, park in the lighted areas. Girls and boys be honest, tell your friends what you think and the reason you do not want to park.

Our teenagers should be encouraged to engage in wholesome activities, those activities which expend energy such as sports, those activities that promote a pure heart. Remember Christ said, "Blessed are the pure in heart; for they shall see God" (Matthew 5:8).

Encourage teenagers to double date and participate in group activities.

To be able to court defensively teenagers should be taught as much as possible about sex. They do not know as much as they think they know. The more a person knows the better able he or she is able to avoid pitfalls.

We should teach our children the Bible, but above all we should live before them the Christian example.

I think we should teach our girls that in general they are better able to control their sexual drive than are the boys. This does not mean that girls do not have as strong a drive or as high a peak as boys. It does mean that usually the onset of the drive is slower and more easily controlled. We must warn our girls not to lead a boy on up to the point just before penetration and say "No." This creates many problems for both the boy and the girl. She may not be able to stop herself and say, "No, you can go no further." The boy may be so emotionally built up and so sexually aroused that he will not accept "no" as an answer. It is at this point that many a girl has yielded from pressure when she said "no" which was not accepted.

Another observation is that a great number have never been told "no" by any female, mother or grandmothers. This boy who has never been denied his every wish will not be denied by the girl who has cooperated and stimulated him sexually during a long petting session.

Teenagers should know that it is possible to be impregnated by any ejaculation near the female vagina. Penetration does not have to occur. External sexual relations or mutual masturbation are not without dangers. Transfer of sperm from the external ejaculation or even the sperm that is present in males secretion during pre-coital excitement is possible.

Teenagers have many false ideas concerning "the safe period" and concerning contraceptives.

It might be good here to answer the question I received last week. "Could you explain periods animals have, such as dogs, cats and cattle? Could we use these to teach our girls?" Many have thought the sero-sanguinous or bloody fluid these animals secrete shortly before they come into heat is the same as a menstrual period in a woman. These people know that dogs, cats and cattle and such like have this flow shortly before coming into heat. This is not the same as a menstrual flow in a woman. Women have what we call menses, monthly cycles or menstrual cycles. Menstrual cycle comes from the word "menes" which means "month."

Animals are in estrus or in heat one, two, three or four times a year depending on the animal. The estrus or secretion is produced by large amounts of estrogen. This is followed by a rise in the follicle stimulating hormones. The animal ovulates when the ovarian follicule is ripe and at this time the female animal will accept the male. Many boys and girls, knowing the proper time to breed an animal, assume that the danger time in a female human is at the end of the menstrual cycle. This is not true. But since they think this is true, they choose the middle of the menstrual cycle to have relations. Unfortunately this is the most fertile time of the woman. Also at this time of the month, when she ovulates, she is also the most easily sexually aroused.

Actually there is no absolute safe time of the month.

This comes about from the fact that the female ovulates about fourteen days prior to the next menstrual flow. Since you do not know when the next menstrual flow will begin, there is no way to be absolutely sure of a safe period.

Since there is no absolute safe period, and since so many advisors are misinformed, seek professional advice prior to marriage for safe contraceptive advice.

I plan an entire lesson on "Birth Control and the Bible," discussing the pros and cons of the various standard methods of contraceptives acceptable in marriage.

Some methods that have come to my attention that have been used in this area that do not work are Saran Wrap, Coca-Cola douches and prayer. This last method was used by a girl pregnant out of wedlock. She could not believe she was pregnant because she said, "I always prayed afterwards I would not get pregnant."

Parents should attempt to keep their daughters from chasing

and pursuing the boys, worrying boys to go out with them and calling them at all hours of the night and day. This practice is becoming more and more common.

Fathers and mothers, tell your sons that some girls plan on getting pregnant to get a husband. Nothing is more desperate or conniving than a sixteen- or seventeen-year-old who thinks if she is not married in the next few months she will be an old maid.

Be aware also that many girls get pregnant out of wedlock to spite or hurt their parents. This fact is attested to by ministers, social workers and physicians.

Let us not be too quick to condemn young people. They have problems. They have the same problems we had when we were young plus the additional problems brought on by the change in communications, change in transportation, change in the mobility of the population making it difficult to promote life-long friendships. Our people are moving all the time. Twenty-five years ago you grew up with and stayed with your friends. Your friends were of many years duration not just a few months. This had a stabilizing and emotional soothing effect. Let us try to understand our young people. Remember we do not have the same temptations they have.

CHAPTER 4

The Dangers of Going Steady

YOUNG PEOPLE often ask, "Why do you not want me to go steady?" Or, "Why is it wrong to go steady?" This will be discussed from the danger standpoint. Not that every person who goes steady makes these mistakes, but certainly I think to be forewarned is to be forearmed. Remember in Exodus 20:14 the Jewish people were commanded, "Thou shalt not commit adultery." Christ reinforced this by quoting this scripture in Matthew 5:27 and adding Matthew 5:28, "But I say unto you, that whosoever looketh on a woman to lust after her hath committed adultery with her already in his heart." This will be discussed later in detail, but certainly we can see that adultery is wrong now and always has been wrong. When we talk about adultery, we are talking about a man and a woman having an illicit sexual relationship and we will not put an age limit which obviously is unnecessary.

We are admonished in Romans 12:1, "I beseech you therefore brethren by the mercies of God that ye present your bodies a living sacrifice holy, acceptable unto God which is your reasonable service." Paul speaks of presenting our bodies. Illicit sexual relations defile the body. I am talking about teenagers and teenagers you remember have mature bodies. They have the ability to conceive. If they do not have these things they do not want to go steady, they are not as anxious to be with the opposite sex. Yet we know the teenager is lacking in experience. The teenager has not learned to control his or her emotions or sex drives. Control comes only by maturity and experience. This control cannot come by the reading of books; though some insight into the problem and possible pitfall warnings can come from parental talks, books, lectures and such like.

To repeat the question, "What's wrong with going steady?" Many of you have heard the admonition to be careful about going steady too young.

Why then do teenagers want to go steady? I think there are really two reasons, one is for social status, the other is social

30

security. Perhaps this steady is the first time the boy or the girl has found someone with whom he or she can talk. Other teenagers respect their peers who have a steady. Older people want social security. The teenager going steady has a certain amount of social security. They do not have to worry about having someone with whom to talk on the phone, about finding someone with whom to go places or about having a financial crisis about each date. So in reality, going steady provides both social status and social security.

However, courting should be a period of learning and preparation for marriage. This is a time when you should learn about the opposite sex, learn how to control emotions and learn how to get along with the opposite sex. It is a time also to learn how to cope with your problems.

If a teenager dates only one person, he relates only to one person. We should teach our teenagers and encourage them to date more than one individual so that they can learn about people who have different moods, various temperaments, and meet with those with different intellectual levels. Unless the teenager has the opportunity to associate with those with different moods, interests, intellectual levels, and temperaments; the teenager cannot possibly know whether the steady date is the right person for them, or if he or she can possibly get along the rest of their life.

We should tell our children that by dating different individuals they can broaden their scope, their personality and their ability to understand others.

I think I should list and discuss some of the hazards of going steady. The first is that going steady leads to familiarity. When a boy and girl first meet, they are bashful and have difficulty talking. Once they meet, they learn to talk and are able to communicate. They become more and more familiar which leads to intimacy. This progresses only a small step at the time and they assume that this gives them license to become more and more familiar. They take more and more liberties. The things that are done on the fiftieth date are not the same done on the twentieth date, which are not those done on the first date. Courting, as other phases of life, is a matter of trial and error, attempts at liberties with rebuffs and counter attacks. Going steady too soon short changes the teenager.

The next question raised is, "What's wrong with petting?" When petting is mentioned, different thoughts come to each of our minds. There is no definition that is agreeable to everyone, but interpret my comments in the light of what you define as petting. All will admit that with petting there is emotional strain. A person loses their self-respect and their reputation by petting. I think the danger is that passion and love is often confused. Petting promotes passion. Often this is mistaken for love. There is a vast difference between love for an individual and passion aroused for and by an individual. We must teach our young people that there is a point in the arousal of their emotions up to which point they can control their emotions. Beyond this point of arousal control is lost. Up to this point the teenager can control the emotion; beyond this point there is no stopping. It is like pouring gasoline on a fire, passions ignite. Emotions are of this nature.

Some scriptures come to mind. "Whatsoever is not of faith is sin" (Romans 14:23). "To him that knoweth to do good, and doeth it not, to him it is sin" (James 4:17). Taking these scriptures and thinking about an individual beginning to pet or petting, and at the same time thinking he will stop at a certain point of his arousal helps us to understand that if he does not stop then he sins.

We are told in James 1:13-15 how temptation springs within an individual, "Let no man say when he is tempted, I am tempted of God: for God cannot be tempted with evil, neither tempteth he any man: But every man is tempted, when he is drawn away of his own lust, and enticed." We find here that when we are tempted it comes from within our own self. It is because we have not put up enough guards whether we are male or female, young or old. All sin comes from this area. "Then when lust hath conceived it bringeth forth sin; and sin when it is finished, bringeth forth death" (James 1:15).

In I Corinthians 10:13, RSV, Saul states, "God is faithful, and he will not let you be tempted beyond your strength, but with the temptation will also provide the way of escape, that you may be able to endure it." There is always a point up to which a person can overcome this temptation. No one can ever plead I was tempted beyond my endurance or that the temptation was greater than I could bear. Like many of our sins we do not hunt for a way of escape. We do not try to find out how to keep from sinning. We go along with the tide. We put up no battle at all to keep from sinning. We should remember Paul's statement in Philippians 4:13, "I can do all things through Christ which strengtheneth me." Here is the source of our strength so that our temptations will be less. We gain strength by Bible study and prayer.

We have children who may or may not ask our advice. Nevertheless we should advise them.[1]

When we are advising our children in reference to sex, we should remember that in general the attitudes of boys and girls differ greatly. Girls usually equate the desire to have intercourse with love. Boys do not think like this, despite what they tell the girl. I have been told many times by the non-virgin girl, "Dr. Pettus, he told me he loved me." Since girls equate desire to have intercourse with love, they conclude that the boy truly loves them if he wants to have intercourse. They are indeed naive. The girls are not aware that the male wants sexual relations because of a strong physical sexual drive, a need for release. This drive is usually not as strong in the female as it is in the male. Our girls do not know these things. Because of the extreme persistence and insistence, girls are persuaded to go too far mistaking passion for love. We should tell our girls that the boys are only seeking a release or a new person to conquer.

I think we ought to emphasize to our girls that no matter how much a boy says he loves her that he will often betray her. Certainly at the time of seduction it is not his plans, but once he accomplishes his goal he can hardly wait to brag about it.

To the male it is a game. One he hopes to win. He hopes to score or at least get to first base. The boy has less to lose than the girl. If he succeeds he has a sense of accomplishment. On the other hand he cannot get pregnant. His reputation is not as likely to be damaged. In certain adolescent, teen-age and adult groups a boy's or man's reputation is enhanced when it is known that he has made out or gone all the way with some girl. This raises his prestige in his peer group.

---

[1] Meade, Beverly T., M.D. "What Advice Should Be Given Adolescent Girls Regarding Boys Importuning for Intercourse," p. 52, Vol. III, No. 9. Sept. 1969, *Human Sexuality*.

A girl must understand that a boy sees this as an accomplishment, and therefore, it is difficult to keep his mouth quiet. If no one knows, he gains nothing. Therefore, he can hardly wait to brag about the girl with whom he has been to bed or what he has done with a certain girl.

The adolescent girl in recognizing that sex is a game with a young man should recognize all the different ways boys and men use to win the game. She should know the various pitches he will use to seduce her.

The first pitch used is as old as the world. "If you love me, you would do it." Here the boy is using "love" to persuade. The counter to this is that the girl should realize that real love is not a matter of making demands. You do not make demands on the one you love. We should teach our girls and boys that love is unselfish, that it is expressed in different ways. The making of demands is not one of the ways of expressing or showing our love. Love includes sacrifice and restraint. The writer of John 14:15 says, "If you love me you will keep my commandments." Christ is telling his disciples that if they love him they will keep his commandments. He did not say if you love me you will let me take advantage of you. This is a poor judgment to which no one should yield.

The second pitch or argument for yielding is, "There cannot be anything wrong with it because it certainly is the natural thing to do." On first thought this may seem to have some merit. However, if this same argument is used in assessing other emotions we come up with the following. Under certain circumstances it may seem normal to murder. You did me wrong and it seems natural for me to want to kill you. The answer is that all emotions and instincts are natural, but we cannot justify murder because of anger, or sinful sexual activity because of lust. Solomon advised, "My son, if sinners entice thee, consent thou not" (Proverbs 1:10).

If a girl who realizes that premarital relations (fornication) is sin, she knows that the person who wants her to practice fornication with him is a sinner and wants her to become a part of his sins. "Now the body is not for fornication but for the Lord and the Lord is for the body" (I Corinthians 6:13). A girl should remember this scripture and I Corinthians 6:18, "Flee fornication. Every sin that a man doeth is without the body; But

34

he that commiteth fornication sinneth against his own body." Remember Romans 12:1 admonishes everyone to "present your bodies a living sacrifice, holy, acceptable unto God, which is your reasonable service."

A third argument or pitch used is "To find out if we are suited to each other." If this is supposed to be a scientific or research project, it is poorly designed. The results would prove nothing. The circumstances and the consequences render this useless.

A fourth argument or pitch is, "Be a sport or be like other girls." The girl should remind the boy he is not much of a sport since he is not taking the chance the girl is taking. What young man would agree to sign a formal statement accepting all the responsibility for any consequences of the act. Rare is the young man who would do this.

Many do not realize that sexual activity cannot be equated with sexual enjoyment. Some argue that they are the same. There is a great deal more sexual activity than there is sexual enjoyment.

Premarital relations (fornication) are not likely to be fully satisfying to a girl. Many of the reasons are the following. There is the fear of pregnancy. This is always in the back of the girl's mind. There is always fear of discovery. This fear detracts from the enjoyment. There is doubt if the boy will be true to his promises of love, fidelity and non-betrayal. There are the guilt feelings. If you deny these are present, you are not being truthful with yourself. If you have been taught all your life an act is wrong, and you commit this act, you know your sin and guilt follows. I have talked with many women in their forties and fifties who still harbored guilt feelings from things they did in their teenage years prior to marriage.

I remember years ago the preacher's wife who came to my office on many occasions because of "nerves" only to break down and cry because of "feeling unclean." While courting the man she later married, she had sexual relations with him on one occasion prior to marriage. Returning from a hayride on which they petted heavily, they parked, they had intercourse and the Christian lady was paying for it ten years later.

Remember to teach your children that marriage requires both a marriage license and a ceremony. Both are necessary to make marriage legal and prevent sexual relations from being sinful.

What should be done in the case of the unwed expectant? The answer some would give, "Get the shotgun, find the boy and force him to marry the girl." I do not feel that this is the answer. The two have made one mistake. To force a marriage that has little or no chance of survival is only compounding the problem. Forced marriages do not hold together. There is much bickering. The child is used as a football. The mother looks at the child and says to herself, "I would not be married if it were not for you." The father has the same thoughts. The child is unloved, unwanted and is raised in an unwholesome atmosphere. A child knows when it is not wanted.

A much healthier way for all concerned is for the unwed expectant to have her baby and place it out for adoption. Place the child in a home that wants it, and allows it to be reared in an atmosphere of love. Abortion, another alternative, will be discussed in a different lesson.

There are twice as many broken engagements in couples who have sexual relations as among couples who do not have sexual relations. The fact should speak loudly and clearly to those engaged. If you want to marry, do not engage in premarital sex (fornication). A man's desire decreases after he has slept with a woman.

The questions arise, "What if it is too late?" "What if you are already going too far?" "What if you are approaching the limits of going too far?"

There are several things to be done. Change your courting patterns. Do not get to yourselves, plan activities, plan on staying in bright places, stay with people and avoid petting. Remember the important thing is not what you did yesterday or are doing today, the important thing is how you behave and conduct yourself tomorrow. Just because you have made mistakes in the past you do not have to continue. Everyone should be able to learn from past mistakes.

Girls, you do not belong to the boys. Boys, remember this. No matter if you have gone all the way. No matter if you are engaged. Remember marriage requires a license and a ceremony.

Remember, it is never too late to change.

We have been speaking as if it were the sole responsibility of the girl to restrain the boy. Boys, it is just as important for you to control your emotions and drives as it is for the girls.

Boys should also determine the limits of propriety. Boys must take the responsibility of not pressuring too much and of not going too far.

Christian boys should remember their obligations to themselves, to the girls they date, to their families and to the Church. Remember, Christian boys, you have your own reputation to uphold. You may ask if boys get bad reputations. They indeed do. Girls do not want to date boys who are known to be fast, who are known to pressure, who pet heavily, or those who insist on having sexual relations.

Remember, boys, there is always the danger of pregnancy. Many a man is in our mental institutions because of guilt—guilt from having fathered a child he never got to see.

Christian boys, remember, many mothers have their daughters on birth control pills. Many college student health centers are dispensing the pill. There is only one reason. It indicates a change in the female role from the pursued to the pursuer or to the planned submitter.

CHAPTER 5

Harlots, Whores, and Prostitutes

WHEN YOU READ this word "harlot" in the Old Testament it brings a picture to your mind. What does it mean in every day language? The expressions "harlot," "harlot's," and "harlots'" are used fifty times in the KJV of the Bible. A harlot is a prostitute and a prostitute is a whore.

The terms "whore," "whoredom," "whoredoms," "whoremonger," "whoremongers," "whore's," "whores," "whoring" and "whorish" are found ninety-seven times in the KJV of the Bible. We are speaking of Biblical terms, are we not? A whore is a promiscuous woman. A whore is a prostitute. The word prostitute is found once in the KJV of the Bible. A prostitute is a woman who engages in promiscuous sexual relations for pay. A prostitute, a whore and a harlot are all the same if we believe Leviticus 19:26, "Do not prostitute thy daughter, to cause her to be a whore; less the land fall to whoredom, and the land become full of wickedness." This passage with the other one hundred forty-seven condemn the whores, harlots and prostitutes who sell their bodies for pay. I am speaking of premarital and extramarital sex.

Many will answer, "I don't know anyone who does this."

Is not swapping sexual relations for a good meal, a night at the movies or at a ball game the same thing?

A girl who will go to bed with a boy because she feels anyway at all obligated to him is prostitute, and a whore. Somehow these terms seem worse to us than the term fornication or premarital sex.

Forty times the word fornication is used in the KJV of the New Testament. Changing the term does not change the action condemned. In I Thessalonians 4:3-4 we are told, "This is the will of God, even your sanctification, that you should abstain from fornication: that every one of you should know how to possess his vessel in sanctification and honour."

Every time the words harlot, prostitute, whore or fornicator are found in either the Old or New Testament it is condemned.

Nowhere is it praised. Note I Corinthians 6:9-10 says, "Know ye not that the unrighteous shall not inherit the kingdom of God?" We all want to inherit the kingdom of God. The remainder of the verse is "Be not deceived: neither fornicators, nor idolators, nor adulterers, nor effeminate, nor abusers of themselves, with mankind, nor thieves, nor covetous, nor drunkards nor revilers nor extortioners, shall inherit the kingdom of God."

CHAPTER 6

Marriage

MARRIAGE is an institution ordained of God. When two people marry, they vow to live together as husband and wife until death parts them.

The Bible teaches very clearly that divorce is wrong. We should teach our children from the cradle that marriage is for keeps. In Matthew 19:3-6 we read:

"The Pharisees also came unto him, tempting him, and saying unto him, Is it lawful for a man to put away his wife for every cause? And he answered and said unto them, Have ye not read, that he which made them from the beginning made them male and female, and said, For this cause shall a man leave father and mother, and shall cleave to his wife: and they twain shall be one flesh? Wherefore they are no more twain, but one flesh. What therefore God hath joined together, let not man put asunder."

Divorce creates problems instead of solving them. Children, families, everyone suffers when divorce takes place.

Matthew continues on this subject, chapter 19:7-9:

"They say unto him, Why did Moses then command to give a writing of divorcement, and to put her away? He saith unto them, Moses because of the hardness of your hearts suffered you to put away your wives: but from the beginning it was not so. And I say unto you, whosoever shall put away his wife, except it be for fornication, and shall marry another, committeth adultery and whoso marrieth her which is put away committeth adultery."

A parallel passage teaches the same lesson in Mark 10:2-12.

God said, "It is not good that man should be alone, I will make a helper fit for him" (Genesis 2:18, RSV). The married enjoy the privileges of marriage, help, conversation, love, sex and freedom from loneliness.

If divorce even enters your mind, remember these things. Marriage is an honorable institution: (1) because God is its author, Genesis 2:22-24; (2) Jesus attended a wedding feast,

John 2:1-2; (3) the Bible says it is honorable, Hebrews 13:4: "Marriage is honorable in all, and the bed undefiled."

The doctrine of celibacy is a doctrine of the devil, not of God.

"Now the Spirit speaketh expressly, that in the latter times some shall depart from the faith, giving heed to seducing spirits, and doctrines of devils; speaking lies in hypocrisy; having their conscience seared with a hot iron; forbidding to marry, and commanding to abstain from meats, which God hath created to be received with thanksgiving of them which believe and know the truth" (I Timothy 4:1-3).

One question that comes to mind is, "Who should a person marry?" You say what has this got to do with sex? It has everything to do with sex because it is only in the state of marriage that sex is right. It is important to pick out the right partner for marriage because nothing is worse than to be bound to the wrong partner. A partner you do not like, one with whom you cannot get along, one who is always provoking arguments about religion, about sex or about any number of things does not help to create the haven of happiness that marriage should be. Certainly picking the right partner is the most important thing I think toward having a happy sexual life. When we go to the Old Testament, we find that Abraham wanted Isaac to marry one of his own kindred. This is a good example for us today when we are advising our young people to marry.

In Genesis 24:1-4 we read, "And Abraham was old, and well stricken in age and the Lord had blessed Abraham in all things. And Abraham said unto his eldest servant of his house; that ruled over all that he had, Put, I pray thee, thy hand under my thigh: and I will make thee swear by the Lord, The God of heaven and the God of earth, that thou shalt not take a wife unto my son of the daughters of the Canaanites, among whom I dwell. But thou shalt go unto my country, and to my kindred, and take a wife unto my son Isaac." He was sending his servant to take a wife for his son and he was making him swear that he would not take a wife for his son from the daughters of the Canaanites among whom he dwelt; where was he sending him? He was sending unto his country to his kindred and he was to take a wife unto his son Isaac. Abraham wanted Isaac to marry one of his own kind, of his own religion, of his own background, of his own kindred. And when Isaac was thinking about Jacob getting married, Isaac wanted Jacob to marry one of the daughters of Laban, his own mother's brother.

Remember later under the law, the Israelites were forbidden to marry the occupants of the promised land. When they came into the promised land, they were forbidden to marry among the Hittites, the Canaanites, the Perizittes, the Hivites, and the Jebusites. These were the occupants of Canaan land. They were forbidden to marry among them because of the problems that it presented. It drew them off into idolatry, they lost their own religion and they forsook the Lord and became idolaters. The Lord forbade them to marry outside the Jewish nation.

Joshua told the Hebrews that they should not marry the inhabitants of Canaan and he tells them why. "They shall be snares and traps unto you, and scourges in your sides and thorns in your eyes until you perish off the good land" (Joshua 24:14).

As we talk and advise our children, let us point out to them that their marriage partner will either help them or hinder them in living the Christian life and being faithful to the Lord.

Nehemiah warned also of the dangers of mixed marriages (Nehemiah 13:23-27). We all know of examples. I can pull from my files the names of dozens of men and women who were faithful members of the Church before they married out of the Church, that is before they married a non-Christian. Many of these are fallen away. Many of these are lost to the Church, they never darken the Church door. Many even though they still attend the Church services, they are very ineffectual Church members. They cannot take a part in any of the worship services or works of the Church because their partner is always holding them back, always critical, always putting up stumbling blocks. Many others even though they may be faithful themselves, lose their family and lose their children. It is difficult to raise children, faithful to the Church if one of the partners does not attend. If mother is a faithful Christian and father is not, then they want to say, "Why can't I stay at home with daddy and if it is not good enough for daddy, why do I have to go?"

Before you marry, you should make sure that you are marrying someone who will help you go to heaven. Someone who will

42

help you be a Christian. Someone who as your partner will help you have a Christian home. My idea of a Christian home is either it is a Christian home or it is not a Christian home. If either the husband or the wife is not a Christian, then you cannot say that it is a Christian home, can you? Before the step into marriage is taken all of these things should be considered.

In my own mind, I am satisfied that members of the church should marry only Christians. I may not prove this to everyone's satisfaction. Many have determined to marry a non-Christian and are not receptive to reason. I think to my own satisfaction it is safe to marry a member of the Church. If you are a Christian, marry a Christian. It is good insurance toward a happy married life and a happy sexual life. It is good insurance toward being able to worship regularly, raise your children in the church, and a big help toward going to heaven, is it not? On the other hand, it is dangerous to marry outside the Church. There are many, many dangers that come to the person who marries outside the Church. We will talk about some of these later. Let me read two scriptures to support my idea that members of the Church should marry only members of the Church. I Corinthians 7:39 says: "A wife is bound by the law as long as her husband liveth, but if her husband be dead she is at liberty to be married to whom she will only in the Lord." Of course we know here he is talking specifically to a widow and says, she is permitted to marry whom she will only in the Lord. If it is good for a widow to marry only in the Lord, if God is no respecter of persons, it would seem that this would also be a requirement of Christians. For further proof go to the Old Testament and find that God would only permit the Jews to marry Jews, a Hebrew was to marry a Hebrew.

We are taught in II Corinthians 6:14, "Be ye not unequally yoked together with unbelievers: for what fellowship has righteousness with unrighteousness? or what communion as light with darkness?" Here we get an indication a Christian should not be unequally yoked with an unbeliever. Some say, "Well, this does not talk about marriage or it is not talking about marriage." I think it is partly. Certainly what closer relationship could a Christian have with anybody than with his wife or with a husband. I think it is sound advice to everyone who is hunting a husband or seeking a wife to choose friends from members of the Church. Of course this goes for everybody, married, single or otherwise. We should choose friends from members of the Church. This serves as a stimulus to act better. We can learn from them. You know you always behave better when you are around people who are better than you. At least if you want to find how people will change, you take even a reprobate and put him with a group of preachers or a group of Christians, and he will change right away and certainly want to give the impression that he is better than he is. I think that Christians should only go places where Christians associate or can go and we ought to enjoy good things. Good advice to the single people and widows is date only faithful dedicated Christians. If you date only a faithful dedicated Christian you will marry a faithful dedicated Christian.

Think about the problems, think about them realistically, certainly it is better to remain single than to lose your soul. One thing we ought also to remember is that marriage is not required. You do not have to get married. Paul teaching the Corinthians, I Corinthians 7:2, said: "To avoid fornication let every man have his own wife and every woman have her own husband." You notice this teaches one wife for one husband. It teaches monogamy as we say and not polygamy. Certainly then this teaches against the group marriages that are becoming popular or that are written so much about today. Group marriages are marriages of two men with two women or three men with two women or two men with three women. This type is opposed to the communal marriage of some of the Hippie groups. Communal marriages consist of ten to fifteen women and ten to fifteen men living together. These never work out and certainly they are contrary to the teaching of the Lord.

There are many common law marriages. This is something that has always occurred. A man and woman just take up one with another and live with each other. Sometimes these stick and sometimes not. Certainly they are not legal, they are not scriptural, because to be scripturally married, you have to be legally married, do you not? We are commanded to obey the laws of the land, and if we do not obey the laws of the land, then we are not scripturally married. Common law marriages are not scriptural and they are not legal. A legal and scriptural marriage requires both a license and a ceremony.

There are a lot of trial marriages today, most popular among college students and younger professionals. Much is written about these in our magazines. The couples say we will try it for a while and if it does not work out then we will separate. These are self-defeating. A trial of a thing is not a good test unless it is right in every way. A trial marriage is not right because there is not a full committal on the part of both partners sexually and emotionally. There is not the emotional tie, there is not the sexual tie in a trial marriage that there is with a legal ceremony. What you have are two fornicators living together. One other problem with this type of marriage is that there is always a chance of a pregnancy. A pregnancy should be the time when both man and woman are happy. When a pregnancy occurs in a trial marriage, this becomes a tragedy. They are not bound together to take care of the child. There are no emotional ties. The child will come to a union where there is no real tie to keep the father, no real tie to make him support the child.

Proverbs 1:10 says: "My son, if sinners entice thee, consent thou not." I Corinthians 15:33, RSV, says: "Don't be deceived: Bad company ruins good morals." Certainly bad company when carried over to our dating partner would be somebody who was not a Christian.

Marriage embraces all the relationships of Christianity. As a Christian, anything you do in marriage has some bearing on your religion. We ought to remember the examples of the Israelites and how when they married the heathen, they were driven into idolatry. You will notice that one of the things that caused them to go astray was marriage outside the Israelite nation. This was Solomon's problem. Remember when you are courting, there is always a possibility of marriage and then there is always a possibility of raising children. We talked two or three weeks ago about a child having the right to expect that both mother and father be a Christian. It is the duty of Christians to raise their children in the nurture and admonition of the Lord. In fact this is a command found in Ephesians 6:4.

One other thing a man ought to remember is that he cannot be an elder in the Lord's church if he is not married to a Christian

(I Timothy 3:4-5). We have to remember that Christianity is a religion of principles as well as a religion of laws. Ask some Christian who has married a non-Christian what his or her advice would be. Does the union help you to keep faithful? Is it a help in raising faithful children? Is it a full and satisfying life? I see many of you every time I come to worship. I know that your mate never comes with you. If you had to do it over again, would it have been better if you had not married, if you had waited and found a Christian to marry who would come with you to worship and would help you raise your children, help sit with them or help you take care of them.

I think it is far better to be a little more patient, to trust in the Lord more, pray more and marry a Christian than to handicap yourself by marrying out of the Church.

We said that you did not have to get married but marriage is for some reason. Genesis 2:18, RSV, tells us that marriage is for company. "It is not good that man should be alone; I will make him a helper fit for him." We usually read about a "help meet for him" (KJV). We should find out that these words mean, I will make a helper suitable or fit for him. Somebody that will fit in with him, be a companion for him.

Genesis 2:24, "Therefore shall a man leave his father and his mother and shall cleave to his wife and they shall be one flesh." Marriage is for company, and marriage is for unity or oneness. It is difficult to have oneness in the home if one person is a Christian and the other is not and will not go to worship, will not read the Bible, will not teach the children to pray, but will do everything in the world to downgrade the Church, criticize the Church, make fun of other Christians and be a constant source of disagreement. It is difficult to have full and happy satisfactory sexual relations if every Wednesday night you have a problem about, "Are you going to prayer meeting with me?" If every Saturday night when studying your Bible school lesson, every Sunday when you are going off to worship, your mate is sitting at home poking digs at the Church. It is hard to come home on Sunday night in a good mood, happy, joyful, loving, as we would say, to face someone making light of our worship experience.

We talked about marriage being for company and for unity, but marriage is for something else. I like this because I think

46

marriage is pleasurable. Genesis 3:16, "Your desire shall be to your husband." This means that the wife has something she is to give to her husband.

Ecclesiastes 9:9, "Enjoy life with the wife whom you love." Enjoy life, this indicates that sex is pleasurable, does it not? Notice we are talking about sex in marriage and all these are to be in marriage. Notice the passages we read, three in Genesis and one in Ecclesiastes talk about enjoyment, company, unity and implies sex is a wholesome thing in marriage.

We have mentioned several times already that sexual relations outside of marriage is condemned. There are many terms that refer to illicit sex, each of these is condemned in the scriptures.

Marriage, as God intended, is honorable and necessary. The Christian home is designed to provide mutual sharings of the happiness that can exist in families.

CHAPTER 7

The Husband and the Home

THE PURPOSE of this lesson is to talk about some Bible truths so that each of us can have a happier home as husbands; so we can be more like Christ would have us be; to help us men be better husbands; to have happier homes. If we are better husbands, then this will make our wives better wives. I have told many of you many times that husbands are like puppies, if you pat them, treat them good they will lick your hands and you cannot chase them away from home. So wives, if you are good to your husbands and kind to them, then you cannot drive them away.

Many, many men do not take the responsibility of being husbands, but it is a man's duty to be the head of the home. This means the head of the home in the following ways: in making decisions, in deciding what should be purchased, in paying the bills, in deciding what the family can afford and keeping up with family affairs.

We read in Ephesians 5:23, "For the husband is the head of the wife as Christ is head of the church." I Corinthians 11:3, "The head of every man is Christ, the head of the woman is man, and the head of Christ is God." I Corinthians 11:8-9, "For the man is not of the woman; but the woman of the man, Neither was the man created for the woman, but the woman for the man." Matthew 19:6 says, "Wherefore they are no more twain, but one flesh. What therefore God hath joined together, let not man put asunder." We see that when a man and woman are married, God joins them together, they are bound together from then on, until death parts them. Because of this, we ought to make sure that we pick out the right wife, the right husband. We ought to teach our children to pick out the right wife or the right husband and teach them that marriage is for keeps and not just a trial thing.

Since it is the duty of man to be the head of the house, he has some obligations and responsibilities.

Ephesians 5:25 says, "Husbands, love your wives, even as

48

Christ loved the church, and gave himself for it." Notice here it is a command that husbands are to love their wives. God never commanded us to do anything that we cannot do. I have heard men say, "I do not love her anymore." When he states this, he is rebelling against God. For God commanded the man to love his wife and if you do not love your wife, you are disobeying God, are you not? This implies that it is possible to love your wife. If you try, if you pray, if you make an honest effort you can love your wife. If you do not love your wife, you are in rebellion against God.

"So ought men to love their wives as their own bodies. He that loveth his wife loveth himself. For no man ever yet hated his own flesh, but nourisheth and cherisheth it, even as the Lord the church" (Ephesians 5:28-29). "Husbands, love your wives, and be not bitter against them" (Colossians 3:19). The RSV says, "Do not be harsh with them." This hits a lot of us. We are not to be harsh with our wives.

Husbands should take the lead and be an example in all religious matters in the home. We know that husbands should be a baptized believer. Christ commands that all should be baptized. "He that believeth and is baptized shall be saved; but he that believeth not shall be damned" (Mark 16:16).

The husband should study the Word of God, he should let his wife and children know that Christ is his Master. The husband should attend all the worship services of the Church. If he does not, he is violating Hebrews 10:25, "Not forsaking the assembling of ourselves together, as the manner of some is." It is a command to assemble and worship.

A husband should honor his wife. I Peter 3:7 teaches, "Husbands, dwell with them according to knowledge, giving honour unto the wife, as unto the weaker vessel." Every man will say you should honour your wife. To this all agree. However, the first part of the verse says we should dwell with our wife according to knowledge. This means we should learn all we can about our wives. We should learn what the scriptures teach about how to treat our wives.

We should learn about the physical make-up of a woman. Many men never realize a woman is different from men. They think differently. They act differently. They respond differently. A man should make an honest effort to learn these things. To

49

make the same mistake for thirty years does not make a man an expert, does it? Often we find a couple who will marry at the age of eighteen. They assume that since they are old enough to get married, that they know how to have sexual relations. The husband thinks he is an expert in the matter of sex and sexual performance. Often what he has learned up to the age of eighteen is about all he will ever know because he does not make any effort to learn more. I think a husband should make a conscious effort to learn more about his wife and how better to perform. I hope this is part of the reason many of you are here tonight.

A husband should learn what it takes to sexually arouse his wife. Think about this. It indicates to me that there is a right way and a wrong way to make love.

A term which frequently comes up is the word, frigidity. You hear men talk about their frigid wives. They say she is as cold as an ice box. They have all kinds of terms to describe this when they talk about their wives. If you define frigidity as the inability to respond, there are very few frigid wives. Most of the time it is because the husband has not learned enough or does not take the time to excite or to prepare his wife. Put another way he is too ignorant to learn how to excite his wife or too selfish to spend enough time to excite her. It is often his fault, if she does not respond.

Often husbands cannot understand why their wives do not get as excited as they did during courtship. Yet often they do not realize that during courtship, this love-making and courting went on for a period from one, two, three, four or five hours. With such lengthy sessions of courting and petting, the girl friend became quite excited. Many husbands think that after one kiss or a minimal of foreplay, the wife should be ready for intercourse.

A constant complaint that I hear from women is that their husbands do not spend enough time in getting them ready or preparing them for sexual relations. Many times I think it is ignorance. Many times I think it is a lack of concern.

I have asked many women with this complaint to bring the husband in to my office for a talk to find out where the problem lies. Very rarely do I have a husband come in to discuss the problem. Men often forget that they are different from women.

We mentioned this before, but we need to point out some of these differences. Men are excited by what they see and think and by past experiences. An illustration is the pin-up pictures that servicemen hang on their barrack walls. They get excited by just hearing a sensuous story. Most women are different. Most women require bodily contact. They require some tenderness, some preparation and they require some show of attention. A man cannot expect his wife to become fully excited if he waits till bedtime before he starts to show any attention to her. A man should remember he should not bring up problems, arguments, troubles or accusations at bedtime. If he starts off good with a courtship after supper and waits till bedtime to start an argument or start to bring up troubles, he turns off both himself and his wife.

A physician friend of mine told me that he tells his patients that the bedroom should be for sleeping and for loving. This makes sense. If you always equate the bedroom with sleep or loving, then you know it is not a place for discussion of problems, arguments, bills, what the children are doing wrong or child discipline. You cannot keep two things on your mind. You cannot be sexually excited when you are worrying about problems, bills and other things. So let us leave our problems outside the bedroom and keep the bed for sleeping and for loving.

Let us talk about foreplay. Foreplay should complement and supplement intercourse. Foreplay can be just as much fun as the act of intercourse. There should also be some afterplay. Foreplay should be a pleasure. It should be long enough and intensive enough for a complete sexual arousal. Think about this. You cannot completely sexually arouse your wife in three or four minutes. Yet oftentimes, women tell me their husbands want them to be ready for intercourse with two or three kisses. Very few women can get excited that fast. Let me repeat foreplay should be long enough, intensive enough for a complete sexual arousement. Later I will talk about some of the ways this can be carried out. For the present we want to say that intercourse should not begin until the wife is properly and fully prepared. Wait until she is ready and eager for intercourse.

If intercourse is begun too soon, there are not enough secretions. There is not proper relaxation of the peri-vaginal muscles, since these relax as the woman become excited and anticipates intromission. If started too soon, intercourse is not pleasurable and may even be painful. The added friction from the lack of lubrication and relaxation leads to premature ejaculation by the male. This is frustrating and disappointing to the wife and embarrassing and ego-deflating to the husband.

A husband should learn to do and to practice the things that will excite his wife. Do the things that please her.

I might stop right here and say that wives should let their husbands know what they like best. They do not always have to say do this, do that, but certainly by the manipulation of the hands, the mouth and the body they can promote by their actions the type of foreplay that they enjoy most. Wives, promote the actions which excite you the most.

I find no scripture that prescribes what is normal for foreplay. Nowhere in the Bible can I find that a man and his wife should do this or that before having relations. No place do I find a specific act engaged in by a man and his wife condemned.

Before I am misquoted on this or accused of teaching something that is not in the Bible, let us consider an analogy. Christ said in Matthew 28:19, "Go ye therefore and teach all nations, baptizing them in the name of the Father and of the Son, and of the Holy Spirit." Here we find that it says go teach, this is a command but He does not tell us how to go. We can ride, walk, fly, run or swim. Anyway we go is all right, is it not? Now if we read some scripture about what a husband is to do about the marriage bed we can find that a lot of things are permissible in marriage. "Marriage is honourable in all, and the bed undefiled" (Hebrews 13:4). "Likewise, ye husbands dwell with them according to knowledge" (Hebrews 13:4). "Let thy fountains be blessed: and rejoice with the wife of thy youth. Let her be as the loving hind and pleasant roe; let her breasts satisfy thee at all times; and be thou ravished always with her love" (Proverbs 5:18). When it says, "Be thou ravished always with her," it means be filled with joy always with her or be enraptured with her. "Live joyfully with the wife whom thou lovest" (Ecclesiastes 9:9). This means enjoy life with the wife whom you love.

In the Song of Solomon, the human breast is glorified. In

52

the eight short chapters of the Song of Solomon, the subject is mentioned eight times with no shame, with no indication that it should not be spoken of and should not be a part of the enjoyment of a man with his wife. Song of Solomon 8:8 says, "We have a little sister, and she hath no breasts: What shall we do for our sister in the day when she shall be spoken for?" Song of Solomon 4:5 states, "Thy two breasts are like two young roes that are twins, which feed among lilies." "A bundle of myrrh is my well beloved unto me; he shall lie all night betwixt my breasts" (Song of Solomon 1:13). Here we find that Solomon was aware of the importance of breasts, between a man and his wife.

We find in all these passages that the marriage bed is honorable, that the bed is undefiled and that a man is to dwell with his wife according to knowledge and that he is to enjoy and rejoice with his wife. We find that a wife is to be feminine, she is to be modest, she is to be lovely and her breasts are to satisfy her husband at all times and he is to enjoy life with her, and according to Solomon her breasts are to be enjoyed.

I think foreplay is a matter between husband and wife. It is for them to decide what they want to engage in, what satisfies them, what excites them and what they give each other pleasure in doing. I think when there is a big difference in the sexual drives of a man and his wife a conscious attempt should be made by the one with the weaker drive to satisfy the partner with the stronger sex drive. If you have a man with a strong sex drive and a wife with a weak sex drive, then she should make a conscious attempt to promote a better attitude toward sex and to enjoy sex more. He should make a conscious attempt to bring her to a higher peak of sexual excitement to do the things that satisfy her and be good to her. I think the sexual appetite, as every other appetite, can be increased by stimulation and cultivation.

There are scriptures which teach this. Read I Corinthians 3:3, "Let the husband render unto the wife due benevolence; and likewise also the wife unto the husband." This KJV may leave doubts but the RSV says, "The husband should give to the wife her conjugal rights, and likewise the wife to the husband." This indicates she has the right to expect to have relations with him. Then it says, "Likewise a wife to her husband." So a husband has the right to expect to have intercourse with his wife.

Verse four, the same chapter says, "The wife hath not power of her own body, but the husband: and likewise also the husband hath not power of his own body, but the wife."

"Do not refuse one another except perhaps by agreement for a season." Do not refuse to have relations except for a season and this has to be by agreement, "That you may devote yourself to prayer but then come together again, lest Satan tempt you for lack of self-control" (I Corinthians 7:5, RSV).

It is disturbing to me to do a pelvic examination on a woman who has been married for years and to find a constricted vaginal outlet; and who, when asked when she last had intercourse, says that it was three or four or five years ago. This is a bad situation. It is in violation of I Corinthians chapter 7. The responsible party has put the partner in position of temptation of Satan. If he is not willing, then he is violating the Scriptures. If she is not willing, then she is violating the Scriptures.

Even if the completion of the act of intercourse is not always possible, an active attempt and a show of affection will increase the desire and the performance. We should cultivate a more active sexual life. Remember it is not distasteful and certainly it is in keeping with Scripture. One other thing we ought to remember is that the frequency of intercourse in marriage is not prescribed except in I Corinthians 7. Here we find it should not be abstained from except by mutual consent.

I have some suggestions here for the husbands. If your wife does not respond as readily or as often as you think she should, she will improve if you will do these things. (1) Make an honest effort to continue the courtship and this means day in and day out, gifts, etc. (2) Never criticize her before others. Proverbs 29:11 says, "A fool uttereth all his mind; but a wise man keepeth it till afterwards." (3) Divide your income with her; it will help improve her attitude. (4) Compliment her. (5) Thank her for the little things. (6) Confide in her. (7) Do not be jealous. (8) Do not be suspicious. (9) Be patient with her. (10) Be understanding with her. (11) Share your recreation hours with her. (12) Although God has made man the head of the wife, never make her feel inferior. She is equal with you before God. (13) Remember wives have problems

54

too. (14) Remember housework is confining, monotonous, repetitive and nerve wracking. (15) Try to realize some of the responsibilities of wifehood and motherhood. (16) Assume the overload that saps the wife's strength. By this I mean help her when you have time. (17) Honor her by showing affection. (18) Notice the little things. (19) Never criticize. (20) Be worthy of her in your actions, in your dress, in your manners and in your conversation. (21) Be clean. It should not be necessary to mention this, but it seems to me that a dirty husband would turn a wife off as quickly as anything. I talk with and examine a great number of men who are dirty; by this I mean have not recently been clean. I am not talking about the day to day dirt which the manual laborer, the mechanic or even the office worker acquires. Every man can bathe each day when he comes home or before he goes to bed.

A man should spend enough time in foreplay to completely sexually arouse his wife. Many men do not do this. One of the most common complaints I hear from wives is that their husbands do not spend enough time in preparation. I think this is a legitimate complaint.

I do not think a man should ever begin intercourse until his wife is prepared, ready and eager for relations.

A husband should learn and practice those things that please his wife. He should learn and practice those things that sexually excite her. A man does not know these when he marries, but if he is smart he will learn what excites his wife very soon. He will do these things rather than being stubborn, ignorant and selfish. He will try to make intercourse a pleasure to her.

Men often forget that there is a big difference between men and women or between the husband and the wife. Remember that husbands are excited by what they think and by what they see. With his imagination and anticipation of sexual relations, a man can become excited.

Whereas, women usually require bodily contact, require foreplay, require talking and require a lot more than just thinking about intercourse. Many men not realizing this want to begin relations too soon, without enough foreplay. We have discussed that we should not bring up problems, should not bring up accusations, should not bring up our troubles at bedtime or near bedtime. Nothing will turn a woman off any faster than prob-

55

lems. You know this yourself. We should not bring up a lot of problems.

I said that a bedroom should be for sleeping and loving. I think this is a truisim.

If you reserve the bedroom for pleasure and sleep, and not equate it with fussing, fighting, arguments and problems then certainly the wife and husband both will be in better mood for relations. A happier home results.

I was told recently that often husbands cannot be cornered. It seems that the only time the man gets still or quiet enough to talk about household problems is at bedtime. This is unfortunate. Try to arrange a time and place for these discussions that do not interfere with the pleasure of the bedroom.

We know that a husband must be faithful to his wife. "Marriage is honourable in all, and the bed undefiled; but whoremongers and adulterers God will judge" (Hebrews 13:4). We said whoremongers and adulterers were those who had extra-marital relations. Modern writers speak of extra-marital relations, but God calls it whoremongering and adultery.

"But I say unto you, That whosoever looketh on a woman to lust after her hath committed adultery with her already in his heart" (Matthew 5:28). A man does not have to run around on his wife to sin in the sight of God.

A husband should support his family. "But if any provide not for his own, and specially for those of his own house, he hath denied the faith, and is worse than an infidel" (I Timothy 5:8). A man who will not work for his wife, who is too lazy to get out and work, and who will not bring home money and support his family certainly cannot expect his wife to be eager and anxious to go to bed with him. These things are part of having a happy home.

Men do lots of things that affect their sex life. We want to talk about some of the things that affect their sex drive.

When Dr. Alton Ochsner, who is a Professor of Surgery, Tulane University School of Medicine and President of the Ochsner Medical Foundation was asked: "Do cigarettes affect the sex drive?" He answered, "Cigarettes certainly do affect the sex drive or capacity. It has been my universal observation that after a person has stopped smoking his sexual capacity

56

is definitely increased. This is almost invariably observed."[1]

Some men who are smoking may not be up to their full capacity as a man because smoking lessens their performance and cuts down on their drive. If smoking cuts down on the drive of a man, how much more will it affect the sex drive of his wife because of the repulsive breath, the repulsive body odor of the cigarette smoker. Do not forget the stained teeth, the stained fingers, the draining sinuses and the chronic cough.

Think about these. Perhaps some of these are the reasons the so-called frigid wife is not anxious to go to bed with her husband.

A question from the audience: "What about a person who chews tobacco?" Answer: "He may not have the stained fingers, nor the cough, but he does have the repulsive breath."

Next, we are going to talk about alcohol. Here is another thing that suppresses the sex drive. Even Shakespeare wrote about this. One of his characters is quoted as saying, "Drink provokes the desire but it takes away the performance."[2] A man should be at his best in order that he may enjoy the relations and that he may better satisfy his wife.

The person who drinks whiskey or beer has a repulsive breath. Did you ever smell a person who drank who did not have a repulsive body odor?

It has been less than two weeks since a woman told me that she just did not want to go to bed with her husband because of the way he smelled. Certainly this will make a husband less desirable to his wife.

Many men get so embroiled in their hobbies that they forget to do all the things we have listed that will increase sexual performance. Whether it be hunting, fishing, making model cars or just reading, you can do these things to excess. Men get so interested in these hobbies that they forget to carry on the courtship, petting and all the things we have mentioned for a normal, healthy, active sexual life.

Some may ask, "Why do men take up so many activities away from the wife and the home?" There may or may not be a

---

[1] Alton Ochsner. *Medical Aspects of Human Sexuality*, August 1969, Vol. III, No. 8, page 87.
[2] *Medical Aspects of Human Sexuality*, Feb. 1970, Vol. IV, No. 2, page 60.

reason. He may have been rejected at home. A rejected husband is a frustrated husband.

Recently a man told me that the reason he was in so many clubs, was that his wife thought that intercourse should take place about once a month. He said that this was not enough for him and since he did not want to step out on her, the only way he could control himself was to keep busy all the time that he was not on the job.

Interfering relatives sometime make for an unhappy marital life. Often a relative in a home is necessary because of financial necessity. More often the relative is there at the insistence of either the wife or the husband. A relative will cut down on the opportunities of sexual relations and the opportunities of free expression of desires and emotions.

Some men take up a lot of hobbies as a refuge because of impotency. They perform poorly and are unable to satisfy their wives so they avoid the conflict instead of seeking help.

There are two types of impotency. (1) One is the man who cannot get an erection. (2) The other type of impotency is relative impotency. This type occurs because of poor past performances or because of lack of confidence or because of premature ejaculation. The husband is ashamed or does not want to show that he cannot perform adequately. Premature ejaculation can be helped. It can be caused from having relations so rarely, that an eager husband who is so worked up sexually cannot hold off an ejaculation long enough to perform adequately.

The treatment for this type of impotency is more frequent and regular intercourse. If you have problems with intercourse one time a month, you should have relations regularly a number of times per week. You should have intercourse as often as you are able to get an erection. By experience many are able to overcome their premature ejaculation problem.

A man should also realize that the failure is not in the penis but a matter of the mind. A wife and husband working together can overcome many problems by more frequent relations. Remember a wife is able to have relations as often as her husband can obtain an erection.

Women are not like men. If they are properly prepared, they can have multiple orgasms. Many can have orgasms one right after the other as long as the husband can sustain an erection. There is no such thing as impotency in a woman since impotency by definition is the inability to perform. Since the vagina is always present, if she has been properly prepared, then she can always have intercourse. She may not always have an orgasm, but as we have said this is not always necessary.

Premature ejaculation can be helped by cooperation, by having more frequent relations and by foreplay with the wife until she is ready and eager for relations. If she is sexually excited almost to the point of orgasm or at least to the point where she is eager to have relations, then there is much vaginal secretion and there is relaxation of the peri-vaginal muscle. The introduction of the penis is aided because of the lubrication and because of the relaxation. If the wife is sexually excited, there will not have to be a long period of thrusting before she reaches an orgasm. This minimizes the premature ejaculation problem.

There are other ways to overcome this problem. I think these should be discussed with your own physician. All the individual problems cannot be discussed here. If you have specific problems, then private consultation would be best.

We talked about some of the beneficial effects of intercourse. We must remember that all the glands of the body are inter-related. The testicles are related to the pituitary and the pituitary to the adrenals and the adrenals to the pituitary. There is an inter-reaction among glands.

Frequent regular intercourse stimulates the testicles, which stimulates the pituitary gland, which in turn stimulates the ovaries, the thyroid and the adrenal glands. When the adrenal glands are stimulated the body releases hydro-cortisone. Hydro-cortisone is the miracle drug in the treatment of arthritis. It is believed by a great number of us that frequent and regular intercourse stimulates the pituitary, which stimulates the adrenal to release hydro-cortisone which can be beneficial in mild arthritis. Certainly the mild exercise in intercourse is also beneficial to arthritis and by way of argument you can say that frequent and regular intercourse could be beneficial in preventing the progression of crippling arthritis to some extent.

Dr. David Reuben,[3] stated that, "No normal heart was ever

---

[3] David Reuben, M.D. *Everything You Always Wanted To Know About Sex But Were Afraid To Ask.*

harmed by sexual activity. Actually, a vigorous, healthy interest in sex and an active sex life is probably the best form of protection against a heart attack." He reasoned that the three major precipitating factors in a heart attack were: lack of exercise, overweight and nervous tension.

If lack of exercise, overweight and nervous tension will precipitate a heart attack, think of the benefits of copulation. They are exercise, muscle maintenance, movement of all the joints of the spine, improved circulation, deep breathing, tranquilizing effect of orgasm, release of pent-up emotions and consumption of about 150 calories per intercourse.

The health addicts like to jog at a rate to make the heart rate increase to over 120 beats per minute. During intercourse the heart rate jumps to between 120 and 160 per minute, just prior to and during orgasm.

Many have said that a single act of intercourse between a man and his wife is equal to a half hour of jogging. I have said before in teaching these lessons that jogging around the neighborhood four times cannot compare with once around the bed.

In comparing an exercise program with frequent intercourse with your wife there is no comparison. Exercise programs are work, they must be planned and they are not enjoyable. You have a tendency to forget them. Sex is none of these.

An active sexual life is an added incentive to keep your weight down.

If one of the biggest burdens on our hearts today is nervous tension, a fully satisfying sexual relationship is the best tranquilizer available. The married know the relaxation and peace of mind that comes from orgasm. Such relaxation and peace of mind is unattainable at any price.

Someone will jump up and say, "Will sex bring on a heart attack?" I do not think sex will harm a normal heart. But suppose you have an abnormal heart. Let me say that if a person's cardiac status has deteriorated to the point that he is on the verge of a coronary occlusion then the straw that breaks the camel's back may be the act of sexual intercourse. Men and women do suffer heart attacks during intercourse. But if the heart is so damaged that this is the final thing that brings on the attack, think of other things like running for the bus, watch-

60

ing a real exciting television show or having a fierce argument that would do the same thing. It does not seem right to give up sex to forestall a heart attack for a short time.

Another question that comes up about health and regular sexual intercourse in males is: "What about prostatism?" About one-third of all men between the ages of twenty to forty suffer from prostate trouble at one time or another. There are two main causes of prostate trouble. One is the pounding of the peritoneal area since the prostate lies at the neck of the bladder. Heavy equipment operators, truck drivers, cowboys, motorcycle riders all have a lot of trauma to the peritineum. This on occasion will produce prostate trouble. The treatment for this is to change jobs and get into an occupation that does not have all the pounding of the peritineum. This usually will solve the problem.

Another common cause of prostatism is constant sexual stimulation without gratification. This results in a bloated, tender prostate. We know that sailors, priests, students, hen-pecked husbands suffer from prostatism more. This brought a laugh from some but this is true. Studies have been made on sailors, priests in the monasteries and students who spend a great amount of time studying without having a sexual outlet. The thing that concerns us most here is the hen-pecked husbands. Men, who even though they are married, do not have frequent or regular intercourse many times face this problem. The treatment for this kind of prostatism for the married is frequent and regular intercourse.

For the unmarried it is a different matter. You have to avoid intense stimulation and another thing would be occasional masturbation. I say that here, because later on we will have a lesson and will talk in detail about masturbation. We will pass it up now except to say that this is one of the treatments.

61

CHAPTER 8

The Wife and the Home

I WANT now to talk about the wife in the home. This is what the men have been waiting for.

Remember the purpose of this lesson is to learn from the Bible how to have a happier home.

Many scriptures that we have studied before we will study again. Remember Titus 2:4 where the older women are to, "Teach the younger women to be sober, to love their husbands and to love their children." Remember the marriage vow that you made: You said that you would love, honor and obey your husband.

If you want to know what love is, we can go to I Corinthians 13. Remember we were talking to the men about things that they should do to make their wives more responsive. Since women have promised to love, honor and obey their husbands, let us see if our wives live up to these things.

They do if they are patient, kind, if they envy not, are not arrogant, if they do not behave themselves unseemly and are not discourteous and do not seek their own, are not easily provoked, and do not think evil, rejoice not in unrighteousness, but rejoice in the truth, will bear all things, believe all things, and are full of hope and will endure all things.

Wives are commanded to love their husbands. It is possible to love a husband because God commands it. I have had many women to tell me that they do not love their husbands anymore. When they make this statement, they are disobeying God's command. Are they not? If you are married to a man and the Bible commands that you love him, I do not think God commands the impossible.

If you do not love him, then you must cultivate a love for him. You must work at it. It is going to take a lot of positive action. Some of the things and ways to do this is by showing him honor and respect.

Ephesians 5:33 says, "The wife is to reverence [or respect] her husband." Ephesians 5:22 tells wives, "submit yourselves unto your own husbands, as unto the Lord." Titus 2:5, "To be discreet, chaste, keepers at home, good, obedient to their own husbands." Notice here that wives are to be in subjection to their own husbands and not to some other men. "Likewise, ye wives, be in subjection to your own husbands; that if any obey not the word, they also may without the word be won by the conversation of the wives" (1 Peter 3:1).

I Timothy 2:9-10 talks about wives dressing modestly. We will not go into what is modest. A wife should dress in such a way that the husband thinks she is modest. No man wants his wife to look like a street walker, a trollop, or a loose woman.

If a woman dresses to the modesty requirements of her husband, this will be probably satisfactory to everyone else. If not then, it is not anyone's business but his or hers.

I do not think we as individuals should set up standards of modesty for other people.

Wives should bear children. "I will therefore that the younger women marry, bear children, guide the house, give none occasion to the adversary to speak reproachfully" (I Timothy 5:14).

Let me summarize: if a wife dresses modestly, if she loves her children, if she is a hard worker, if she respects her husband, if she obeys him, if she honors him, if she is chaste and discreet and a keeper of the home, and if she makes him the king of the home, then this sets up a good atmosphere for good sexual relations.

Let us take a little time and read and discuss I Corinthians 7:2-5, "Nevertheless, to avoid fornication, let every man have his own wife, and let every woman have her own husband." This will stop pre-marital sex and extra-marital sex and all the attendant evils. Verse three: "Let the husband render unto the wife due benevolence; and likewise also the wife unto the husband." The RSV reads: "Render unto the wife her conjugal rights." Verse four says, "The wife has not power of her own body, but the husband; and likewise also the husband hath not power of his own body, but the wife." This means that marriage is a reciprocal agreement between the two and they cannot deny one another these rights. Verse five says: "Defraud ye not one another, except it be with consent for a time, that ye may give yourselves to fasting and prayer; and come together again, that Satan tempt you not for your incontinency." Defraud means to take away. A man has certain rights, his wife has no right to deny him. She has no right to deny him sexual relations. Likewise also the husband does not have the right to deny his wife sexual relations. Verse five tells us the reason we should not do this is so that Satan will not tempt you for your inability to restrain your lust.

Remember I Peter 3:7 commands husbands to "dwell with them according to knowledge."

God is no respecter of persons. I think that most Bible scholars will agree that if husbands are to dwell with wives with all knowledge that a wife should dwell with the husband with all knowledge. She has the obligation to find out about his physiology, about his temperament, about how to treat him and how to best satisfy him so that the two working together can have a happier life.

Remember we have mentioned several times that there is a basic difference between men and women that men are stimulated by sight, by pictures, by fantasies, by indirect stimulation, whereas usually women require more direct bodily contact.

Men are usually more rapidly stimulated than their wives. We want to remember that all of these are learned processes. This means that you are not born knowing how to have normal relations. Most people think that if they are old enough to marry they know how to have relations. They are not taught correctly. Rather, from birth to adulthood they are taught many false ideas, under the guise of morality and etiquette. If it were not for the erroneous teachings, I think there would be no frigidity, no confusion, no inhibitions and no sexual incompatibilities.

Instead humans would do as the animals, do what is enjoyable and do what comes naturally.

Teach a girl sex is dirty, wrong, degrading, painful, unenjoyable, and what can you expect?

Since these are learned responses, I believe all of us can unlearn our bad habits, our bad responses and learn better habits and better responses.

Everything we learn is through the sense of sight, smell, taste, feel or hearing. Whether it be mathematics, chemistry, physics or farming, our senses are our aid in learning.

There are five ways in which a woman can stimulate her

64

husband and there are five ways she can be stimulated by him. These are the five senses by which we receive everything. We receive by sight, by touch, by smell, by taste and by hearing.

The very first impression that your husband made upon you was by the way he looked at you. You saw him and either liked him or disliked what you saw. This is the first contact you had with him. This was the first way he stimulated you, a positive stimulation or a negative stimulation.

A woman can stimulate her husband through sight by the use of clothing. Women from the very beginning of time have known this. However, some of our modern women forget this. I think a woman should dress like a woman everyday at work, in the privacy of her home and in her bedroom. A woman should dress differently at these different places.

I would advise a woman to find out what her husband likes and dress accordingly. If he likes thin night gowns, black or red bikinis, short and revealing or long and covering clothes then dress in whatever is to his liking. This makes sense. What would you think of a woman whose husband likes sheer see-through night wear and she comes to bed with a flannel gown from her neck to the floor, wearing a bra and a pair of panties? She is not trying to stimulate or please her husband.

Women in Bible times knew that dress stimulated men. "And, behold, there met him a woman with the attire of an harlot, and subtile of heart" (Proverbs 7:10). Present day wives can profit from this.

Since I am talking about stimulating your husband through the sense of sight, remember husbands are stimulated at times by a nude wife. I find no scripture to illustrate this but since they are one flesh I know this is right. I feel that these statements on dress should be sufficient. I think a woman should dress to please her husband.

There are other ways to enhance the sexual stimuli of your mate. One of these is by the use of lights. The use of soft warm lights in the bedroom can be sexually stimulating. Remember the prostitutes who practiced their profession in the red light district. They knew by using red lights they looked more alive, more pleasing and more sexually stimulating to men than if they had put in blue or green lights. Green or blue lights make a woman look dead and undesirable. Take notice in your bedroom use warm pink lights instead of blue or green lights. Undertakers know this effect on emotions. Did you ever go to a funeral parlor that did not have warm pink lights. Many wives do not take advantage of these basic well known facts. In all romantic novels soft warm lights are used in describing a romantic bedroom scene. This has already become a conditioned response for men. I think a wife should make an effort to enhance this response and to bring about all the stimulating influence she can bring to bear on herself and her husband. We know soft warm lights are associated with romance.

Summarizing these thoughts on sexual stimulation by sight remember a woman owes it to her husband to keep herself as physically attractive as possible. This means to dress like a woman and to make herself attractive, to keep herself neat and to make herself pretty in his eyes. What one husband likes another may not. Each wife should study and know her own husband, what he likes and the types of clothing he wants her to wear.

The use of sight to stimulate a man can be used in reverse. A man usually does not like curlers. He does not like a sloppily dressed wife, wearing rags or worn out clothes. He does not like unkempt hair. Very few men want an excessively fat wife. I believe the laugh I just heard was my wife. I have always told her that when she got fat I would lock her in the closet.

I believe if women would remember these points on stimulation of your husband through the avenue of sight and practice then a happier home would result.

The next way we can learn or be stimulated is by the sense of smell. Recent research[1] in neuropsychology and in neurochemistry has pointed out that the rhinencephalon, which is a part of the brain that has to do with smellng, has an important part in the regulating of emotions. This means a person can be stimulated positively or negatively by what they smell. Positive stimulation in sex is what we want without a doubt— a clean body, clean clothes and perfumes. Negative stimuli are body odors, halitosis and smelly clothes. You can readily see

---

[1] What Is Sex Appeal? David N. Rotnavale, M.D. *Medical Aspects of Human Sexuality*, p. 63, April 1970, Vol. IV, No. 4.

the difference between the two types of stimulations.

Solomon knew this, Song of Solomon 1:12-13, "While the king sitteth at his table, my spikenard sendeth forth the smell thereof, A bundle of myrrh is my well beloved unto me he shall lie all night betwixt my breasts." Solomon knew about the use of perfumes, how that they stimulated him and how they served to satisfy him.

The perfume industries know this from the names of perfumes they have such as: Tabu, Intoxication, Aphrodisa, Intimate, Discreet, Tigress, Temptress, Shocking, Possession and all the other names of perfumes you know. All of these indicate they are associating their perfumes with sexual stimulation. If you remember these and make good use of them you will come out to the good in trying to satisfy your husband.

I have been told when teaching this, that I should tell you husbands that every once in a while it would not hurt for you to bring a bottle of perfume to your wife. This serves two ways. You get in good stead with her for bringing her the perfume. When she uses it, the perfume will be stimulating to you.

The sense of smell cannot be separated from the sense of taste. If you have a cold and you try to taste something, you do not get the same taste as when your nose is open.

You may ask, "Can you be stimulated by taste?" Certainly you can. We know men are stimulated by taste. The lips taste different than the skin. Breasts taste different from the neck. The neck tastes different from the ear lobes. We know this, yet we often do not consider it when we think about what stimulates us sexually.

This is also a reciprocal thing. If a man receives stimulation from his wife's mouth, she in turn is being stimulated by him. Since I mentioned several portions of the body that taste different you may ask, "Aren't there some portions of the body forbidden to taste?" I find no scripture that teaches this. Let us consider Proverbs 5:18-19, "Let thy fountain be blessed; and rejoice with the wife of thy youth. Let her be as the loving hind and pleasant roe; let her breasts satisfy thee at all times; and be thou ravished always with her love." Here we find Solomon talking about the use of the breasts or the tasting of the breasts as a portion of the love act. I find no scripture that forbids the tasting or kissing of other parts of the body. In our culture kissing is a part of love-making and is sexually stimulating to both partners. As a conditioned response which we have learned from books, novels, radio, television and billboards we expect to be sexually stimulated when we kiss or are kissed.

The next sense through which we are stimulated is the sense of touch. As a means of arousing and intensifying the sexual pleasure this should not be overlooked. It should be exploited to the fullest. The sense of touch has two sides, just as the sense of taste and the sense of smell has two sides. When a wife touches her husband, she stimulates him and she in turn is stimulated by him. Learn to touch those parts of the body that are most stimulating. Touching the husband's body especially his genitals will stimulate the husband and his response should be stimulating to the wife. There are no areas forbidden to the touch. I have talked with many women who have been quite appalled because their husbands wanted to touch and fondle their entire bodies. I have found no scripture that puts a limit on where the hands or mouth are to be placed in foreplay. Wives should let their husbands know what they want and what they enjoy. If your back itches, you tell your husband where and how to scratch it. Be just as candid with him during foreplay and he will be able to stimulate you to a higher peak of excitement. He will do only those things pleasing and exciting to you and will refrain from those things that have a negative effect on you. A wife has to tell her husband on occasions not to do certain things or to encourage him in other acts of foreplay. Something which is quite stimulating on occasions may turn you off at other times.

Use all these avenues of stimulation and you arouse your mate to a higher peak of excitement.

The fifth sense by which we are stimulated is the sense of hearing. I have found that during the courtship couples talk a lot. They continually profess their love, compliment their partner and sweet talk for hours. Yet after marriage almost no talk is engaged in during the foreplay. This is not right. By the sense of hearing, we are stimulated. Wives should tell their husbands what they want to hear. Husbands want to be told

68

they are loved, they are happy and that they are enjoying the love-making.

Wives compliment your husbands performance. Compliment his body. Compliment his organs.

The sense of hearing is a two-edged sword. Husbands and wives can be turned off by what they hear. I have had men tell me their wives lose all sex appeal if they come out with, "How do I know that you really love me?" or " You've been drinking again."

Let us consider the question, "How do I know you really love me?" This is often a difficult question to answer even when you are sitting and talking. It is almost impossible to answer during the foreplay when the husband is doing all he can to show his love and affection. If he must stop and itemize one, two, three he must get your mind off of stimulating and concentrate on proving a point.

Sexual arousal is really what we want to learn to accomplish. In each of these discussed five areas many stimuli can be introduced. Conditioned responses play a great part. A woman can be quickly responsive to stimuli as their husband. Women who have learned what stimulates them or how they can stimulate their husbands concentrate on the stimuli. If you do this, you will become a better lover and will have a happier married life.

Women should develop confidence in themselves. This is important. No matter what you are doing, you need confidence in yourself. You would not have married your husband if you had not loved him. He wants to satisfy you and you want to satisfy him and wanting to satisfy him you can satisfy him.

You must take the positive approach. You need to broaden your outlook on sex by reading, by talking with your husband or by discussing things that are bothering you. Do not do this in the bedroom. Be open to criticism, be receptive to suggestions and try new ways of stimulation. Remember positioning during coitus is irrelevant as long as mutual satisfaction occurs. Remember the frequency of intercourse is up to the individuals who are engaging in it.

There is a big difference in sexual drives. Since often there is a big difference in the sexual drives between a man and his wife, an effort must be made to bridge the gap. The one who has less drive must make an honest effort to become more interested in sex and try to become a better sexual partner.

I have misplaced the source of this quotation, but I think it is appropriate at this time. "The wife will find her spouse is better able to perform the love act if she indicates by her receptiveness, by fondling him, by caressing his body, by kissing him passionately, and by generally indicating she is as eager for his love as he is for hers. She need not apologize for expressing her natural desires for sex gratification. Once she understands that the normal husband appreciates a wife who is active in love making, who teases and stimulates him, and who is not ashamed to show him by her physical coital movements, in addition to verbally expressing it, her enjoyment of the sexual episode, she need have no fears of his seeking satisfaction elsewhere."[2]

---

[2] Source unknown.

CHAPTER 9

Dyspareunia and Vaginismus

WE have been talking about ways to have a happier married life. We talked about various ways wives can stimulate their husbands and can be stimulated by their husbands. This was talking about preparation for having sexual relations but sometimes a woman says, "I can't have sexual relations because it hurts." The medical term for this is dyspareunia which is a big long word translated, "unhappily mated as a bedfellow" or commonly known as painful intercourse. There are different kinds of painful intercourse. Painful intercourse can either be physical or psychogenic, which means that there could be a physical reason why intercourse is painful or there can be an emotional or psychogenic reason why intercourse is painful. There are two types of painful intercourse that are physical. The first one we would speak of is initial painful intercourse. Initial painful intercourse called initial dyspareunia, almost always occurs in the first intercourse; notice, I said almost, because first intercourse is not always painful because various things enter into this. Every woman does not have the same diameter of vaginal outlet. Every woman is not always in the same mood to have relations her first intercourse. It is not necessarily always painful but most of the time it is and this is called initial dyspareunia. This lasts only a few days after marriage. If it lasts longer than a few days then it is more than initial dyspareunia. The treatment for painful intercourse right after marriage is to take hot tub baths and to refrain from having relations until some of the soreness clears up. If painful intercourse persists, then there could be other reasons for this and this is what we call secondary dyspareunia and if it persists for a long period of time or if it begins after a normal length of time of non-painful intercourse then there must be some other cause. There are a great number of causes that would have to be eliminated. Some possible causes are (1) leukorrhea which is the white discharge of vulvo-vaginitis, which is an infection of the female organs, (2) a shortened

71

vagina, (3) infections of the cervix, (4) proplapse, which is a dropping down of the tissues of the female organs, (5) some abnormalities of the ligaments supporting the uterus, (6) old lacerations or scars in the vaginal vault, or the top portion of the vagina, (7) tumors of the genital track, (8) stenosis or scarred narrowing of the vaginal outlet, (9) gonorrhea, which we will talk about later. We will probably have half a lesson on the great scourge and real problem of gonorrhea and syphilis, gonorrhea being one of the causes of secondary painful intercourse, (10) neuritis, (11) cystitis, inflammation of the bladder, (12) hemorrhoids, (13) anal fissure and (14) abscesses. All of these can be causes of secondary painful intercourse. Someone will say, "What percentage of painful intercourse is physical?" You would have to take different statistics. One doctor may run a study with his clientele and find one out of ten have a physical reason for painful intercourse. Another physician's study may show that ninety per cent of the painful intercourse is physical. This does not mean that one doctor is overlooking something, but that his practice is different. The educational level, the economic background and the teaching background of each physician's patients are different. Certainly there is a group of women who have painful intercourse due to physical reasons and these should be diagnosed and treated so that marital relations can be improved.

The other type of painful intercourse is functional or psychogenic. This is by definition painful intercourse without a special or organic cause. Since there is no physical or organic cause, the physical examination is negative, you do not find the infection, the tumors or the scarring, you do not find the shortening of the vagina, you do not find the prolapse and you do not find any of the things that you can find in the physical type. Therefore, the treatment for this type is different. It usually requires a relearning process. A woman has learned to respond to sexual relations by having pain, so she has to unlearn this. She must relearn that this is a normal relation. She as a woman is required and should enjoy intercourse. Really this is a negative learning process. You have to unlearn something. You have to unlearn all the bad and then learn all the good qualities. It requires a change in attitude and a woman, as long as she has it in her mind that she is not going to enjoy intercourse or that she does not want to sleep with her husband, no matter how much you talk to her or how many physicials or how many doctors she sees, she is still going to have pain. One of the treatments for this is proper preparation of the woman. She must be properly prepared for intercourse. We discussed what a husband is to do to bring his wife to a higher peak of excitement, so in this area, I think it is left up to the husband for proper preparation. Women must also become less inhibited. If you are inhibited, and plan not to enjoy intercourse then I am sure you will not. This is true in everything, whether we are talking about relations or something else. We have to have our mind made up that we are going to enjoy having relations and a change of attitude to become less inhibited. Another way is to anticipate pleasure. Be positive that this is going to be a pleasurable act. Tell yourself you are going to enjoy it, and that you are looking forward to it.

Anticipate and learn to achieve orgasm. You will say, "Well, if you can't, you can't." This is not necessarily so because all of these things are learned processes, I think. We can learn things that we make up our minds to do. You say, "How can I do this?" There are various ways to do this: by reading books, by consulting people who are knowledgeable in the field, by experimentation and various other ways. It is a learned process.

There is another condition that gives rise to problems in sexual relations and this is called vaginismus. This is really a spasm of the circum-vaginal and peri-vaginal muscles. Almost everyone who has studied this has said it is psychological in origin. It is probably a conditioned response. The woman has learned that if the introitus or the opening to the vagina is touched with the hand or penis to respond with muscle spasms. You can readily understand that if the muscles around the vagina go into spasm when the vagina is touched, intercourse will be painful. Since it is psychological in origin and since it is a conditioned response, to treat the condition there must be a unlearning process and then a relearning process. Someone says, "Is this always a result of an emotional conflict or a neurosis?" Not necessarily so, you can have a conditioned response and not even know the origin. I think you can compare it with the blink of the eye. You cannot keep from blinking your eye if someone flips their hand toward you. You automatically blink. A number of women may not know why the muscles go into spasm if something comes near the vaginal outlet. The treatment for this is for the woman herself to learn to dilate the vaginal orifice with her fingers or with lubricated cylinders that are available. By consciously trying to relax and knowing that she will not hurt herself, frequently these conditioned responses can be overcome. Learning to overcome this will not make a woman like her husband nor will it make her enjoy intercourse, but it will help her cure some of her phobia about painful intercourse. When she gets over the idea that intercourse must be painful, then she may develop a desire for and a pleasure in having sexual intercourse with her husband.

CHAPTER 10

Pre-Marital and Extra-Marital Relations

I WANT to talk about pre-marital and extra-marital relationships. I cover this in the section to the women not because of prejudice or anything of that nature but this seemed a good place to discuss this portion. I think this primarily because I hear so often about women questioning their husbands about previous sexual experiences. I would like to caution all wives and warn you against questioning your husbands about any sexual experience prior to marriage because what possible good can it serve if he confessed to every thought that he ever had that was wrong or laid out in detail any experiences he may have had. I think in the same realm we ought to remember that we ought not volunteer any confessions about pre-marital relations or pre-marital experiences. Let me speak also here when I speak of pre-marital or extra-marital relations, I am speaking of fornication and adultery and we do not want to dress up the language by calling it pre-marital or extra-marital relations. The Bible speaks plainly of it as being fornication and adultery. It is condemned. It is wrong and it always has been sinful and always will be sinful, but the fact that it is wrong does not keep us from talking about it. If you have made mistakes, you cannot undo them but certainly you can forget them and not be inhibited or have guilt feelings about pre-marital experiences. This is a great problem with people that I have talked with who have had pre-marital experiences and have guilt feelings concerning them. They oftentimes do not seem to realize that they can get forgiveness for these and oftentimes the Lord has forgiven them many years ago and yet they have not forgiven themselves. This creates a lot of problems and lots of worry. I do not think there is a month that goes by that I do not have this brought up by somebody in talking with them as to what is worrying them and what is their biggest problem. When I ask what seems to come up in their mind most and why is it that they are unable to sleep, oftentimes it is this very thing that they did maybe ten years ago or five years ago that is still on their conscience.

The same things goes about confession and talking about extra-marital relations or adultery. If you have committed adultery since your marriage, I think that the thing to do is to seek God's forgiveness and certainly God will forgive this. God wants to forgive us our sins. I John 1:9 says: "If we confess our sins, he is faithful and just to forgive us our sins, and to cleanse us from all unrighteousness." This includes lying, stealing, adultery and everything. If God will forgive us our sins and wants to forgive us, then we ought to be willing to forgive ourselves and not live in an atmosphere of guilt and burden and always be bothered with this. Luke 6:37 says, "Forgive, and ye shall be forgiven." Ephesians 1:7 says: "In whom we have redemption through his blood, the forgiveness of sins, according to the riches of his grace." We have no doubt that we can receive forgiveness for extra-marital relations. The seventh commandment of the Decalogue of the Law of Moses in Exodus 20:14, "Thou shalt not commit adultery." There are other sins such as stealing, lying, being covetous. The Lord will forgive us of one as quickly as he will forgive us of the other sins. He would not want us to continue in this, would he?" I Thessalonians 4:3 instructs: "For this is the will of God even your sanctification, that ye should abstain from fornication." I Corinthians 6:9-10 states, "Know ye not that the unrighteous shall not inherit the kingdom of God? Be not deceived; neither fornicators, nor idolaters, nor adulterers, nor effeminate, nor abusers of themselves with mankind, nor thieves, nor covetous, nor drunkards, nor revilers nor extor,tioners shall inherit the kingdom of God." Notice this is all in the present tense talking about those who continue to deceive, those who continue to be covetous and to steal. This also intimates that if we steal and quit stealing we can be forgiven and we can be pleasing to the Lord. We all remember the story of Christ and the woman taken in adultery and what he told her. He did not condemn her, she had already been condemned but, he told her to go and to sin no more. Somebody might say, "Why are you talking to us like this?" It would be a most unusual group this large with this many married people here to not have had the sin of adultery to have been engaged in since marriage. So we talk about this as a personal thing so that if these things have

76

occurred, we want to stop them and we do not want to continue to live in sin. I think also we ought not to accuse a mate of extra-marital relations or adultery. Do not ever accuse a mate without absolute positive proof of infidelity. I have been told by husbands, "I might as well have been sleeping with a woman because my wife accuses me of it when I am late or when I can't account for every minute of my time when I am not at work." A continual accusation by a husband or wife can, I think on occasions, give credence to the thoughts that, if I am going to be accused of it anyway, I think I might as well go ahead and do it. If you have had extra-marital relations or if you have committed adultery—the news stories like to call it extra-marital relations—do not repeat it and seek God's forgiveness and forgive yourself, then let that be the end of it. Make a resolution not to ever do it again. If you are at the present time having extra-marital relations, stop them, seek God's forgiveness, forgive yourself, and do not repeat them.

One piece of advice to all, do not take it on yourself to write an anonymous letter or make a phone call to report on someone you think or someone you know is cheating on their mate. This would serve no good, would it? Many homes have been wrecked by phone calls, by notes and often without justification and even if it were true, reporting it to a mate and breaking up a home would not serve you any good and certainly would have not helped that home. It is none of your business or my business what someone else is doing except we have an obligation to talk with them. If there is someone we are worried about, our obligation is not to tell their mate but to go to that person and talk to them. If we go speak to the individual, not to some other persons, these things I think, may help. Often times homes are destroyed and certainly never any real purpose is served in reporting to a wife that her husband is stepping out on her or to a husband that his wife is stepping out on him. Perhaps the time that it occurred was the very last time the individual would do it or was planning on doing it. Maybe they had already made up their mind that they would not engage in infidelity again and this was the occasion you took to report it or to bring up suspicion and wreck a home.

CHAPTER 11

The Menopause and the Christian Home

THE MENOPAUSE is the cessation of the menses or the
monthly menstrual cycle. This is a normal occurrence in the
life of a woman. It is normal for the menarche or beginning
of the menstrual cycle to occur in the early teens. Therefore,
every woman here tonight is pre-menopausal, menopausal, or
post-menopausal. You are either before the age of menopause,
at the age of menopause or after the age of menopause. Every
man here that is living with a woman is living with a woman
in one of these stages. It is good for us to learn about these
and some of the problems that a woman has at this time.
Remember I Peter 3:7, "Likewise, ye husbands, dwell with them
according to knowledge, giving honour unto the wife, as unto
the weaker vessel, and as being heirs together of the grace
of life; that your prayers be not hindered." If a husband is to
obey this, he must learn about the menopause. Women should
learn what they can about it so they will not be ignorant. There
are many, many books about the menopause, but I talked with
a woman recently and she said, "I never read a book about
that, and I am not interested in learning about that." This
does not seem right to me. It seems to me a person would
want to learn as much about their body as they can, to know
what is happening and why.

Someone asks, "Is it scriptural to talk about the menstrual
periods or menopause?" I think that it is. Read Genesis 18:11-14.
The reference to the menopause in Genesis 18:11 reads, "And
it ceased to be with Sarah after the manner of women. God
promised Abraham to "return—according to the time of life and
Sarah shall have a son."

This is reaffirmed in the New Testament, in Romans 4:19,
"And being not weak in faith, he considered not his own body
now dead, when he was about an hundred years old, neither
yet the deadness of Sarah's womb." Speaking of Abraham's
sexual prowessness, the Hebrew letter states in Hebrew 11:11,
"Through faith also Sarah herself received strength to conceive

78

seed, and was delivered of a child when she was past age, because she judged him faithful who had promised." She was past the menopause, as we would say today. Other scriptures mentioning the menstrual cycle are Isaiah 30:22, "Ye shall defile also the covering of thy graven images of silver, and the ornament of thy molten images of gold; thou shalt cast them away as a menstruous cloth; thou shalt say unto it, Get thee hence." The menstrual cloth at that time was worn by women. Today we would say "sanitary napkins," but they were to throw them away as women do today. We read in Lamentations 1:17, "Zion spreadeth forth her hands, and there is none to comfort her; the Lord hath commanded concerning Jacob, that his adversaries should be round about him; Jerusalem is as a menstruous woman among them." Here he makes reference to the woman having her menstrual cycle. Ezekiel 18:5-6 tells us, "But if a man be just, and do that which is lawful and right, And hath not eaten upon the mountains, neither hath lifted up his eyes to the idols of the house of Israel, neither hath defiled his neighbor's wife, neither hath come near to a menstruous woman." Under the old law there were certain times that a woman was unclean, one of these times was during her menstrual cycle. Leviticus 18:19 teaches, "Also thou shalt not approach unto a woman to uncover her nakedness, as long as she is put apart for her uncleanness." So under the old law a man could not have relations with his wife if she was having her menstrual cycle. Leviticus 20:18 continues, "And if a man shall lie with a woman having her sickness, and shall uncover her nakedness; he hath discovered her fountain, and she hath uncovered the fountain of her blood; and both of them shall be cut off from among their people." It was a responsibility of both of them. We know this is talking about a man and his wife, because it was wrong for a man to commit adultery. It was wrong for a man to uncover the nakedness of any woman that was not his wife and we read many passages in Leviticus to prove this in times past. Read Leviticus 15:32-33, "This is the law of him that hath an issue, and of him whose seed goeth from him, and is defiled therewith; And of her that is sick of her flowers, and of him that hath an issue, of the man, and of the woman, and of him that lieth with her that is unclean." If you look up the words translated sick of her flowers, it means menstruating. There are many, many passages in the Old Testament concerning the menstrual cycle. We read two references in the New Testament concerning the menstrual cycle of Sarah being past the age or post-menopausal. Leviticus 15:19-27 gives the laws concerning the uncleanliness of women and when they are unclean. I think it is right to talk about menstrual cycles and menopause. Since it is mentioned in the Bible, I do not think it is wrong to talk about it at home. I do not think women should be put down or ridiculed at the age of menopause. They need more sympathy at this age because of the things that are occurring in their life. We recognize that when our daughters begin their periods they are fractious, irritable, easy to cry and difficult to tolerate. We recognize this and say this is a part of growing up.

It takes much longer than a year to pass through the menopause. Irritability, sensitivity, incompatibility, hot flashes, the tiredness and aching of the joints, inability to sleep and depressions are some of the symptoms associated with the menopause. Many women have difficult times at the menopause. This time of life varies with different women. Some have prolonged periods of irritability, hot flashes, tiredness, aching joints, sensitivity, insomnia, depressions and other menopausal symptoms.

To reiterate the menopause is the cessation of the menstrual cycle. The menopause occurs naturally or artifically. Naturally the menopause occurs when the ovaries which produce the female hormones quit functioning. This is not a sudden thing in the natural state. It is a gradual cessation of the production of female hormones which we will call estrogen. This is a broad general term for the female hormone.

The other type of menopause is the artificial menopause produced by surgery or by irradiation. The surgical procedure that will produce menopause is a simple hysterectomy. The simple removal of the uterus. This will stop the menses but leaving the ovaries in place, the woman will not have the symptoms of estrogen deficiency until the normal cessation of the production of estrogen. You can also stop the menstrual cycle by the removal of the ovaries and leaving the uterus there. This will stop the menstrual cycle but, will also produce suddenly a surgical menopause with all the symptoms of the lack of estrogen which we will talk about later. The most common type of surgery done is called a complete hysterectomy which includes the surgical removal of the ovaries, tubes and uterus, more commonly called a bilateral salpingo-oophorectomy. This includes the removal of all of these and it produces a surgical menopause at that time.

The other kind of artificial menopause is produced by irradiation of the ovaries with X-rays or Radio-active Cobalt. This destroys the function of the ovaries without surgery. This is done very rarely these days but it is used on occasions where there are certain cases of malignancy.

You may ask, "What causes the menopause naturally?" This is caused when the ovaries, the female organs that produce the female hormone estrogen, quit functioning. The ovaries are replaced normally by scar tissue in the aging female. What do the ovaries secrete? We say again, "They produce estrogen." They begin secreting estrogen shortly before the menarch or when the menstrual cycle begins in the young girl. It is the estrogen that produces the enlarging of the breasts, the subcutaneous fat pads on the hips, the legs and the thighs. Estrogens cause a little girl to begin to look like a woman. Estrogens produce a hairless complexion. Estrogens produce the pliable complexion of the teenage girl. Estrogens in the teenager also triggers the development of the uterus, the vagina, the vulval lips and the clitoris. The whole process is under the control of the pituitary hormones we call gonadotrophins. It is also the estrogens that are responsible for the female state of mind. This is a difficult thing to define but you know women think like women and I think it is because of the estrogens that they have in their bodies. At the natural menopause when the ovaries start playing out you get a reversal of these processes, the breasts begin to sag, there is a loss of the fat pads, there is a loss of fat in the subcutaneous tissue and the growth of hair increases, this is all at the natural menopause. There are changes in the lining of the vagina and changes in the vaginal secretions. They become thinner, lesser amounts and they are less lubricating. Also with the loss of estrogens often a woman goes into a depression.

"Does every woman approaching menopause need treatment?" is quite a common question asked. I would think that if a

81

woman is symptomatic, if her periods are irregular, if her periods are scanty, if she is having hot flashes, if she is easily fatigued, if she is having palpitations of the heart and the other physical signs, dryness of the skin, dryness of the scalp, loss of secretions, thinness of the vaginal mucosa, painful intercourse, all of the things indicating she is suffering from menopausal symptoms, then I think she would benefit from replacement estrogen therapy. The treatment is the use of cyclic estrogen therapy. Either it is given for so many days per month in conjunction with the estrogen cycle she is already having in her body but is now deficient, or it is given by injection.

Someone may ask, "Do estrogens or female hormones cause cancer?" I do not think that this has ever been proven. With the widespread use of estrogens, if there were any correlation between these, I think it would have been apparent already. On the other hand, certain estrogens are used in the treatment of female malignancy, especially female malignancy of the breast.

Another question that comes up is, "Where do you get the estrogens that are given to patients?" These are either produced synthetically, starting with a raw chemical and producing the estrogens, or most commonly prescribed are natural soluble estrogens, those obtained from pregnant mare's urine. Pregnant mares secrete large amounts of estrogens in the urine. These are concentrated, separated and marketed as soluble natural estrogens. The most popular estrogens on the market is Premarin. These are the little yellow or purple pumpkin seed hormones that women talk about taking. The name Premarin comes from the contraction of the three words, *pre*gnant *mare*s *uri*ne. This is the most popular prescribed natural occurring estrogens on the market.

We have been talking about natural occurring menopause which will naturally occur to all women. However, some women do not get to go into natural menopause. They have what we talk about as a surgical menopause, when the ovaries are removed surgically. The question comes up, "What happens then, when a woman is suddenly deprived of her estrogen or hormone supply?" Well, the symptoms come about quite suddenly, before the woman leaves the hospital. She starts having symptoms of estrogen lack. The symptoms usually appear two or three days after a hysterectomy in which the ovaries are removed. A woman will start to have hot flashes and night sweats, fatig-ability, headaches, palpitations, emotional stress and depression. Those who have experienced this know that it is real. These immediate symptoms that come on right after surgery are all preventable or almost preventable by estrogen replacement, simply by giving female hormones. The symptoms we are talking about come on rapidly, but later on there are other symptoms if a woman gets over the initial stage of immediate symptoms. They are delayed symptoms of estrogen lack and these come on over a period of weeks and months unless female hormonal therapy is instituted. These signs are vaginal atrophy, in which the lining of the vagina gets thinner and the opening of the vagina becomes smaller. This produces the dyspareunia (painful intercourse) that we have talked about before. There is loss of elasticity of the vagina and if you lose the elasticity of the vagina painful intercourse follows. Low back pain is often one of the later symptoms of estrogen lack. Apathy occurs, where the woman just wants to sit and do nothing. Her voice becomes coarser, depression occurs and there is a loss of vitality. These later symptoms are just as real as the immediate symptoms. They are oftentimes overlooked because they are not quite as dramatic as the hot flashes and the palpitations. Yet they can produce a lot of problems.

I bring these up because often a woman will have a hysterec-tomy, and when she has all the immediate symptoms she knows she needs some hormones. She is interested in taking her hormones for a few weeks, or a few months or even a year and then she will get off of them and will not get her prescription refilled. She will not go back for her check-ups. She begins to develop later symptoms and really does not associate these with lack of estrogen. Unfortunately lots of physicians do not recog-nize these are due to estrogen lack. These long term estrogen deficiency symptoms come on after the body of the female has been deprived of estrogen over a long period of time. These also occur in women who have gone through the menopause naturally.

Another finding is osteoporosis, a condition in which the bones lose their calcium. They become softer. They break easier. We can all remember our grandmothers, how stooped they became and actually became shorter in height because their verterbra were compressed together by the muscles creating a constant pressure compressing the backbones. This occurs because of the loss of calcium and phosphorus from the bones. Hence women get shorter as they get older. This is one of the findings of long term estrogen lack. Chronic backache is one of the symptoms. This does not come on one year after surgery but this is two, three, five, ten, twenty or thirty years after surgery or after the normal menopause. These women get spontaneous compression vertebral fractures from a minor fall or a sneeze. They may not even be aware of a fracture. They may think they have a catch in their back but later X-rays may reveal a previous spontaneous fracture. The patient upon questioning may say, "Well, I had a backache for a while." Some of these fractures apparently are not acute but come on slowly. Since they are compressions, the muscles just squeeze the verterbrae together slowly.

Another symptom of long term estrogen lack is incontinency. A woman, because of the sagging of the muscles that support the bladder and vagina, the loss of muscle tone and the loss of support begins to have stress incontinence. Not because she has anything wrong with her bladder or bladder neck, but because she does not have the support she needs; so that when she sneezes or coughs, she will wet herself. When she picks up something heavy, she will wet herself. These things can be patrially prevented by staying on hormones and keeping good muscle and fibrous tone. They cannot always be cured by being placed on hormones once they have occurred.

Another finding is senile vaginitis. This occurs from the long term loss of estrogen. The vaginal muccosa becomes thin, easily infected, easily traumatized and dry. Intercourse requires supplemental lubrication. Invariably women seem to pick a poor lubricant that aggravates the condition.

You may ask, "Can estrogen prevent all these changes?" Unfortunately, estrogen cannot prevent all these changes. If it did we could give them and keep women from ever getting old. They would never show any of the tell tale marks of aging. It does not seem right for a woman's ovaries to play out at the age of forty and for her to have to live another forty years without female hormones. I think a woman should receive supplemental estrogens to stave off the aging process, to feel

84

better and to feel younger.

Women will do everything in the world to stay young, except often they will not go to the right place for help. They exercise, join health clubs, diet, go to Weight-Watchers and Tops, eat all kind of special foods, take vitamins and do everything in the world to stay young. They will use all kinds of face creams, hand lotions, mink oil, estrogen creams, Queen-B Jelly and aloe compound. You will agree if you listen to the television over a period of time and note the things that are geared to keep women young. Often one estrogen pill a day will do more than all these other things.

Women in order to appear young will use all types of bras, corsets, waist pinchers and pads—all of these to keep a youthful shape. Often an estrogen pill a day would be of more help.

They will undergo cosmetic surgery, have their nose corrected, their faces lifted and their fat pads changed. They will do everything they can to their hair with wigs, dyes and tints and hairpieces. Their use of clothes to appear young is without limit. I fear many are missing the boat by seeking help at the wrong places.

There was a survey of 314 women who had had hysterectomies, with removal of the ovaries which produced what we call a surgical menopause. These 314 were asked, "How has your operation affected your sexual drive or sexual performance?" Ten of them said, "It had decreased." Forty said, "It increased." Two hundred sixty-seven showed no change. Now this is an evaluation by the woman herself, but it would seem in talking with them that the investigator found that those who had had an enjoyable sex life before surgery had it afterwards. Forty out of the 314 said that their sex life had improved. Most of these attributed the increase of enjoyment to the loss of fear of pregnancy. Those women who did not experience an improvement in sexual enjoyment often were the ones who had no desire before surgery. These women frequently used the surgery as an excuse not to have relations at all.

This type of a reaction is not limited to wives. Men who have had surgery or a heart attack will often use these as an excuse to keep from having to have relations with their wives. By the same token women who do not enjoy intercourse and whose husbands have had a heart attack often will fain an interest in her husband's heart when in realtity she is seeking an excuse not to have relations.

I remember asking a woman who had a hysterectomy if her sex life or performance had changed after surgery. She said there was no difference. However, upon further questioning she answered, "I've never refused him." This woman only tolerated sex. You would not expect any type of surgery to help this type of woman. You would not expect the removal of anything to change her attitude toward sex, her performance or her husband.

Let me tell you of some of the diseases that estrogens are beneficial in helping to prevent. Estrogens apparently help protect a woman from heart attacks. It has been found that the pre-menopausal female has fewer heart attacks than the post-menopausal female. In the post-menopausal females, those who are kept on estrogen replacement therapy have fewer heart attacks than those who are not. Most physicians think the estrogen is the protective factor.

Other data suggest this. If a large group of men who have had a heart attack are alternately placed on high doses of estrogens and the others are not on estrogens, then the estrogen-taking group has fewer recurrent heart attacks. There is a hitch. You cannot get a male to stay on large doses of female hormones because of the side effects. These are loss of potency, enlargement of the hips, and gynecomastia (enlargement of the breasts).

Estrogens seem to offer some protection against the symptoms of gout, and the progression of athero-sclerosis and cerebral arteriosclerosis (hardening of the arteries of the brain).

We have discussed the beneficial effects in the prevention of loss of calcium and phosphorus from the bones which we term osteoporosis.

Estrogens have a place in the management of cancer of the breast in the post-menopausal female. I have seen multiple metastatic lesions of the lung from breast cancer disappear in a few weeks. I have seen the pain from metastatic bone lesions of carcinoma of the breast stop. I am not saying the cancer was cured, but the patient's symptoms were palliated and she became more comfortable.

The question is asked, "Do all women need female hormones?"

Some physicians will answer that none of them do. They refuse to prescribe them, taking the stand that grandmother got by without them and their patients should too. I disagree with this group of physicians. I also disagree with the group of physicians who advocate such high doses of cyclic estrogen therapy that their non-hysterectomized patients keep menstruating until past eighty years of age. This is done by giving estrogens twenty-one to twenty-five days straight and then giving a progesterone hormone with the last five days of the estrogens. Upon the cessation of both of these hormones a withdrawal menstrual cycle will occur. One can keep the woman menstruating on to sixty-five, seventy-five or eighty years of age providing she still has her uterus and providing the hormone level is kept high enough.

Most of us physicians take a moderate position. We like to protect the woman, yet not burden her with monthly withdrawal bleeding. One of the problems of provoking withdrawal bleeding is the woman is frightened of having a cancer.

In the post-hysterectomized woman one may have to use androgens or male hormones in addition to estrogens to control their hot flashes. Other benefits of androgens to the female are an increase in the elasticity of the vagina, enlargement and increased sensitivity of the clitoris and increased libido or sex drive. All of these are quite beneficial to the married woman.

The adrenal glands which are small hormone producing glands are situated at the superior poles of the kidneys. Throughout a woman's life they produce both estrogens and androgens, female and male hormones. Sometimes they produce an excess of androgens over estrogens. This is the reason some post-menopausal females develop a deepened voice and excess hair. The giving of estrogens to the post-menopausal female helps to counter these effects.

Before going further let me give some words of advice to the husband who is living with a wife who is near, at or just post-menopausal. Let me advise you to be a little more patient and a lot more understanding. To the woman who is having menopausal symptoms do not use them to make the entire family knuckle in to you. Rather seek help from your physician.

I think also a great number of things are blamed upon the menopause that should not be. Menopausal women want to blame all their problems on the menopause, as if it were a big bugger. Women should remember the menopause is a part of life instead of something apart from life.

Surgical menopause is also a sterilization procedure, but for the woman who comes to menopause naturally the question is asked, "How long must birth control practices be continued?" To be safe the woman should practice contraception for twelve months after cessation of menstruation. If after eleven months a period occurs contraception must be practiced another twelve months.

Another quesion frequently asked is, "What about taking birth control pills and female hormones at the same time?" It is alright if they are taken the same way. Each time you take a twenty-one day cycle birth control pill take a hormone tablet. The same time you leave off the birth control pill leave off the hormone tablet. The menstrual flow occurs at the same time it would occur if only the birth control pill was taken.

In summary the menopause is a Biblical subject. It is a treatable condition in which many of the symptoms and complications can be relieved. Husbands should be sympathetic. Wives should be realistic and seek professional help. Remember our goal is a happier married life.

CHAPTER 12

The Male Climacteric

I WANT to talk about the male climacteric. This is the male counterpart to the female menopause. The male climacteric is the male change of life. It is not as easily recognized as the female menopause because there is no cessation of menses. In fact, a great number of people deny that there is such a thing as the male change of life. Many of us have seen how obvious it is in some men. It is much more difficult to treat than the female menopause.

The male in his late forties or early fifties who does experience the climacteric may attempt to prove to himself his virility in one or more of the following ways: (1) go off the deep end in his pursuit of some younger female; (2) seek to be around younger people; (3) dress a lot more youthfully; (4) cut his hair in a style worn by younger groups; (5) be attracted to youthful activities. Brother Ira North, a minister, frequently warns the men of the congregation of the danger of the "foolish forties."

This is not something new. David was about fifty years old when he had his illicit relationship with Bathsheba. He was a man past middle age which may account for the incentive for his sin.

There are many symptoms of the male climacteric. As I list them, do not jump to the conclusion that you have them all or that surely this is the reason your husband has been as he has lately. The various symptoms of this clinical syndrome are mental and emotional depression, sexual conflict, loss of potency, apathy, worry, insomnia, loss of concentration, irritability, melancholia, loss of confidence, physical decline, easy fatigability and antisocial behavior.

Every person has some of these symptoms; but if a man at the right age develops a majority of these symptoms it is probable that he is suffering from the male climacteric, from the sudden decrease in circulating male hormone.

If a man in his twenties or thirties has a business, emotional or social defeat, he usually does not worry or let it get him down. He looks on life as a beginning with years ahead to accomplish many things. His outlook for the future is good. If he is the corner pharmacist, he dreams of owning his own drugstore chain. If he is a car salesman, he dreams of owning his own agency. If he is a salesman, he thinks of having an entire sales force under him.

On the other hand take a man in his forties or fifties who is suffering from the male climacteric. If he suffers from a heart attack, develops asthma or diabetes mellitus, requires major surgery or must be put on bifocals, he often considers this a nail in his coffin. He becomes depressed and apathetic. Progressively, symptoms develop. His sexual drive and ability decrease. His attitude toward his wife changes, and she in turn is affected and is disappointed. A wife can help a man who is having these symptoms. She can combat them. She can counteract the loss of interest in her by doing all the things we talked about in our lesson on The Wife and the Home. We have discussed how a wife can sexually stimulate her husband. If the husband is declining in his interest toward her, then she should make an added effort to stimulate him sexually, to give him confidence, to win him back to be the man he was when he was pursuing her actively. This puts the treatment on the wife.

On the other hand, if she does not do these things, then she just adds to the problem.

Dr. John Hampton, who is Associate Profesor of Psychiatry, University of Washington Medical School in speaking about the loss of libido, which is the sexual drive in the male said, "The male is particularly responsive to visual imagery and stimuli; and the wife who has allowed herself to become dowdy, overweight and less than sexually appealing, is a frequent contribtuor to the mid-life slump in the husband's sexual response to her."[1]

Husbands will agree that unless their wives try to keep themselves attractive and desirable there is loss of sex appeal. With the loss of sex appeal there is loss of libido in the partner. A man needs continual reinforcement of his sex drive instead of a continuous stream of things that tend to stifle it.

---

[1] Hampton, J. L., M.D. Loss of Libido. *Medical Aspects of Human Sexuality*, May 1969, p. 102.

A man's drive diminishes with age naturally. There comes a point when he is no longer stimulated. This point comes earlier in some lives than it does in others. The Scriptures record an example. King David lost his sexual drive, his ability to perform. I Kings 1:1-4: "Now King David was old and stricken in years; and they covered him with clothes, but he gat no heat. Wherefore his servants said unto him, Let there be sought for my Lord the king a young virgin; and let her stand before the King, and let her cherish him, and let her lie in thy bosom, that my Lord the king may get heat. So they sought for a fair damsel throughout all the coasts of Israel, and found Abishag a Shunammite, and brought her to the king. And the damsel was very fair, and cherished the king, and ministered to him: but the king knew her not." Here we find King David has passed the middle-aged fling age. He had gotten into old age. He had arrived at the point where he had no hormones at all. He could not respond to the fair maiden who stood before him, who cherished him and who lay in his bosom.

Solomon spoke of this time of life. Ecclesiastes 12:5: "They shall be afraid of that which is high, and fears shall be in the way, and the almond tree shall flourish, and the grasshopper shall be a burden, and desire shall fail." Man's desire ultimately fails because he has a drop off in androgens (testosterone or male hormones). There are physical signs that indicate this. This is a slow gradual process. We know it comes on faster in some individuals than in others. If its onset is recognized, a man should not become discouraged, thinking his sex life is at an end.

Remember in an earlier lesson I pointed out that frequent regular sexual relations stimulate and will prolong ability of an individual to have relations. So when this onset is recognized instead of decreasing, efforts should be made to increase sexual activity.

Testosterone is produced primarily in the testes. The physical signs of decrease in testosterone are the following: atrophy of the testes, atrophy of the penis, higher pitched voice, thinner beard, depression, irritability, loss of height, breast enlargement and flushes. Most can understand the decrease in size of the testes and the penis as resulting from the loss of testosterone. The other findings are from the same condition. Loss of height comes from the decrease in size of the verterbrae because of loss of calcium and phosphorous from the bones. Since the adrenal glands produce female hormones (estrogens), and since there is a diminution in the circulating androgens, there is a relative increase in the former giving rise to the higher pitched voice, loss of beard and breast enlargement. The irritability, depression and flushes are caused by relative rapid decrease in circulating hormones.

The hot flush in the male is not a common symptom. When it is present, it usually comes out only on direct questioning. The patient has attributed the symptom to some food, worry, anxiety or nerves.

You may wonder why a male becomes feminized after his testes quit secreting testosterone. There is a reason why the hips get bigger, the breasts enlarge, the voice becomes higher pitched and there is loss of hair on the face and body. The reason is that the adrenal glands produce both estrogens and androgens. In early life the testes secrete an over-abundance of androgens which suppress the body's response to the estrogens. When the androgen level drops the adrenals continue to secrete estrogens to which the body responds. The giving of males testosterone will counteract many of these changes.

These same body changes occur in the chronic alcoholic with cirrhosis because estrogens are metabolized in the liver and when the liver function is impaired there is an increase in estrogens.

To the male the most important symptom of decrease in androgens is he loses his ability to perform. The treatment is the giving of testosterone. If given by mouth most of the hormone is destroyed in the intestinal tract without being absorbed. It can be given by sublingual lozenges or by intramuscular injection. The injections can be given as aqueous suspensions that must be given frequently or in lipophilic solutions that last from three to six weeks.

Unfortunately male hormones will not ameliorate all the symptoms or reverse all the processes. They will help the irritability and depression. They will help him obtain and sustain an erection. They will cause a decrease in breast size and relieve all the flushes. They will prevent further loss of calcium and phosphorous but will not reverse the process. You can give enough to coarsen the voice, but not enough to cause complete regrowth of the beard.

There are some things hormones will not do. They will not change a non-sympathetic wife which is often the man's greatest problem. The wife who makes fun of him, who belittles him, who makes fun of his inability to perform as a male, who makes disparaging remarks about the size of his penis and other remarks of this nature presents a tremendous problem to a man. No, hormones will not help a man cope with this type of wife.

Shakespeare had Henry IV,[2] say, "Is it not strange that desire should so many years outlive performance?" This is true. It seems no matter how old a man becomes or how impotent he becomes, he still has the desire in his mind to perform. This inability to perform is the thing that brings the patient to the physician. It is of no use to help a husband perform better if his wife is not interested.

Since I have both husbands and wives here, let me comment by saying this should be a cooperative thing. If your husband is interested in performing better and if you are interested in him, do those things that will help him perform. Encourage him in the things that will help him. Encourage him to seek medical treatment. Do those things we spoke about that will stimulate your husband. If your husband is declining, he needs more stimulation than he did in his younger years. To do these things makes for a better and a happier married life than to make fun of him, to tell him to forget it or to say that is something of the past. No matter how much you tell a man to forget it, he does not forget it. He remembers his youth and there is nothing more pitiful than to talk with a man who has passed to the point where David was when he did not respond at all.

You may ask if testosterone is used in cancer. The male with cancer of the penis, prostate or testes would not be given testosterone because it would stimulate its growth. However, the male with cancer of these organs is more interested in living than in getting an erection. His problem is not impotency but survival.

---

[2] Shakespeare, William, *Henry IV*, II, 4.

CHAPTER 13

Sexual Perversions

THERE IS much in the Bible about perversions. This is a timely subject because three or four times a week we have television programs about perversions. Many of you may not recognize some of the things that they are talking about. You also may not recognize that there is a big problem in America with sexual perversions. You may not know perverts have started their own churches which have known perverts as preachers. There are places in California where their avowed purpose is to take over the entire county government in order to legalize homosexuality. There is one county in California with thirty-seven percent of the adult population practicing homosexuals.

We have been talking about normal sexual drives and how and when they should be satisfied. We have found that they are to be satisfied only in marriage. The Bible lists many sexual perversions or abnormal sexual acts.

Homosexuality is a common term for a condition in which men or women have driving emotional and sexual interest in members of the same sex. Hetrosexuality is the condition in which men or women have emotional and sexual interest in members of the opposite sex. Some common terms for homosexuals are queens, lesbians, inverts and gays. The Bible has always condemned homosexuality. "Thou shalt not lie with mankind, as womankind; it is abomination" (Leviticus 18:22). "If a man lie with mankind as he lieth with a woman, both of them have committed an abomination; they shall be surely put to death; their blood shall be upon them (Leviticus 20:13). These are teachings under the Mosaical Law against homosexuality and the punishment for committing the act was death.

In the New Testament homosexuality is condemned. "Do you not know that the unrighteous shall not inherit the kingdom of God. Do not be deceived, neither the immoral, nor idolaters, nor adulterers, nor *homosexuals,* nor thieves, nor the greedy, nor drunkards, nor revilers, nor robbers will inheit the kingdom of

God" (I Corinthians 6:9, RSV). Here we see that homosexuality is a sin. It is wrong.

Homosexuality is not a disease. I point this out because many homosexuals want to claim they are sick and that they could not help from becoming a homosexual. I find no place in the Bible where a disease is condemned. The same goes for drunkenness which is also condemned and which also I do not think is a disease. Many claim alcoholism is a disease. Since homosexuality is a sin, we should know about it so we can teach our children not to drift into it. We must teach them it is wrong, that it has always been wrong and will always be wrong no matter how popular and widespread homosexuality becomes. Legalization will not make it right.

As you are well aware, our television programs quite frequently intimate homosexual acts are being practiced. They speak of homosexuals openly and in many sections of our country homosexuality is practiced openly.

Remember in Genesis 19:1-25 where Lot entertained two angels and how the men of Sodom came and demanded that they be allowed to know the men that Lot had in his house. They demanded that the men be brought out and given to them so that they could have relations with them. Remember Lot offered these men his own daughters. They refused, refused to accept Lot's daughters because they were perverts. They wanted the men. They attempted to force their way into Lot's house. Angels blinded them. It was at this time that Lot was told to flee with his wife and two daughters. After this the cities of Sodom and Gomorrah were destroyed by fire and brimstone. The sin of these homosexuals of Sodom and Gomorrah was prevalent. Sodomy today means the relationship of a man with a man, a man practicing anal intercourse with another man.

Many of you were in the military service in the past and had to hear read at least once every six months the Articles of War. Remember it was emphasized that no man was to be in bed with another man. Remember the penalty for Sodomy was discharge from the service.

The men who practiced Sodomy are known as Sodomites. Read: I Kings 14:24, I Kings 15:12, I Kings 22::46, and II Kings 23:7. If you read some of the new so called translations, instead of calling them Sodomites, they are called male cult prostitutes. This is an ambiguous term, but when you read this you know it refers to those who practice the sin of Sodomy.

Paul refers to this sin when he speaks of the sins of the Gentiles in Romans 1:26-27, "For this cause God gave them up unto vile affection: for even their women did change the natural use into that which is against nature: And likewise also the men working that which is unseemly, and receiving in themselves that recompense of that error which was meet." The Catholic Confraternity Version translates this last phrase, "receiving in themselves the fitting recompense of their perversity." Paul is speaking about perverse sexual relations.

I want to emphasize that homosexuality is sin. I have shown that any sexual relationship other than a man with his wife is a sin. The practice of homosexualism is a relationship not between man and wife, therefore it is sin.

After listing a group of sins including homosexuality that bar a person from heaven, Paul says in I Corinthians 6:11, "And such were some of you: but ye are washed, but ye are sanctified, but ye are justified in the name of the Lord Jesus, and by the Spirit of our God." He indicates that this is a forgiveable sin. Just as the Corinthians who had practiced homosexuality were able to be forgiven, those today who have engaged in homosexual acts can be forgiven.

James 1:14-15, RSV, teaches, "But each person is tempted when he is lured and enticed by his own desire. Then desire when it has conceived gives birth to sin; and sin when it is full grown brings forth death." The desire to have relations with man can be present, but a man does not have to yield. If a man does not yield to temptation, he is not guilty of sin.

I Corinthians 10:13 tells us, "There is no temptation taken you but such as is common to man, but God is faithful, who will not suffer you to be tempted above that ye are able; but will with the temptation also make a way of escape, that ye may be able to bear it." From this we know a person is not obligated to yield to his impulses to have abnormal and perverse relations.

I Timothy 1:9-10, RSV, instructs, ". . . the law is not laid down for the just but for the lawless and disobedient, for the ungodly and sinners, for the unholy and the profane, for murderers of fathers and murderers of mothers, for manslayers, immoral persons, *sodomites,* kidnapers, lairs, perjurers and whatever else is contrary to sound doctrine. . . ." Note we find the law is against immoral persons and sodomites.

Some of you may ask, "Why do you make such a to do and why bring this up? We have no homosexuals in this area." This is not true. We have many clubs in our city where homosexuals gather. There are many places and parks where they meet. Phychiatrists report that in the general population of America five percent of the adult population are practicing homosexuals. In a population that has this many homosexuals it behooves us to be careful with whom we let our children have contact.

The Boy Scouts of America are well aware of this and investigate their troop leaders and those in authority to make sure that homosexuals do not get in position where they can lead and influence boys into homosexuality. They keep files on homosexuals and on leaders who have propositioned boys.[1]

Homosexuality is widely practiced in many areas—notably New York, California and Florida.

In 1970 I clipped an article from the *Nashville Tennessean,* a daily newspaper, which reported on a homosexual church in California with a twenty-nine-year-old avowed homosexual as its minister. The church had 348 members, seventy percent were male homosexuals, fifteen percent were lesbians and the remainder were relatives or friends. With churches teaching and practicing homosexuality and attempts to gain control of county politics, we have problems in America.

Let me say one homosexual act does not make a homosexual. Many people will on one or two occasions have made a mistake and engaged in a homosexual act. This does not make them a homosexual. Like any sin forgiveness is possible. Remember temptations can be overcome. A person does not have to continue to practice these sins.

I say this so that if any of my audience has guilt feelings because of having committed a homosexual act or has practiced homosexuality over a short period of time, you will know forgiveness is possible.

The Bible speaks of other sexual perversions. I guess the

---

[1] Personal Communication with Mr. Ward Akers, Boy Scouts of America, Nashville Office.

most commonly mentioned perversions of the Old Testament is beastiality or having relations with an animal. "Neither shalt thou lie with any beast to defile thyself therewith: neither shall any woman stand before a beast to lie down thereto: it is confusions (Leviticus 18:23). "And if a man lie with a beast, he shall be surely put to death; and ye shall slay the beast, And if a woman approach unto any beast, and lie down thereto, thou shalt kill the woman, and the beast: they shall surely be put to death; their blood shall be upon them" (Levicitus 20:15-16). We see this is not new. This is not as common a practice in our cities as in rural areas. Yet we see it is condemned in the Bible.

For completeness let me list a number of different perversions. Though not specifically condemned by the Scriptures, these acts are sinful.

Pedophilia or child molestation is a sexual perversion in which satisfaction is derived only from molesting a child.

There is a perversion called fetishism which is a sexual obession with an inanimate object, wherein a man collects leather shoes, women's panties, or some other object that has sex appeal to him as a sex symbol. Often we read stories about some man who is found to have a room of shoes, a trunk of panties and such like. I think the last time I read about a fetish was the man who had a rented hotel room and had it full of women's shoes he had stolen. To most of us this seems unbelievable but it does occur.

The perversions of transvestism is the adaption of the dress and often behavior of the opposite sex. This is also done by homosexuals who are practicing perversions with each other.

The most common perversion that results in the arrest of individuals is exhibitionism. In this perversion an individual exhibits or shows his genitals to the opposite sex. Usually it is a man exposing himself before a female. Some however, derive satisfaction from masturbating or urinating in public or by appearing in public with insufficient clothes. These individuals often have problems of inner conflict and are quite difficult to help once they are exhibiting or showing themselves. Since these actions are not in keeping with the teachings of the New Testament and the teachings of Christ, they are sinful.

Another perversion is voyeurism in which an individual derives sexual satisfaction from seeing sex organs or sexual acts. The common name for voyeur is peeping-tom.

There is a group of perverts called sadomasochists who derive pleasure from the infliction of physical or mental pain either on others or themselves.

Zoophillia is a term applied to those who have an abnormal love for animals.

There is a group who derive their satisfaction from having intercourse with a corpse. These are called necrophilliacs.

There are those who are not satisfied by normal sexual responses and seem to be oversexed. The term nymphomania is applied to the female. Satyriasis is applied to the condition in the male.

A perversion specifically condemned over twenty times in the Bible is the sin of incest. Though not mentioned by the term incest, I find condemnation of the man who has relations with his wife's mother, with his aunt and it lists all the other relatives.

We have a new perversion today. Though not specifically condemned in the Bible, I know it is a sin. I speak of telephone obscenity. These individuals achieve sexual gratification by using obscene words on the telephone.

Another cult is arising in America today. I speak of the increasing numbers who engage in and practice group sex. All recognize this as sinful and because of this, an increasing number of people are suffering guilt from having engaged in this degrading activity.

The remaining portion of this lession is not about perversions, but because some of you may think the subject to be dealt with is, I want to teach it here as a contrast. Note that all perversions listed were by individuals who were not married. By contrast I do not think there are restrictions on sexual activities between a man and his wife. Any sexual activity that is agreeable and pleasurable to both man and his wife should produce no guilt feelings. In our lesson on pre-coital foreplay we found Bible examples and implications that it was right to engage in foreplay.

I have counselled with women who are quite upset because their husbands wanted to kiss them on their body in areas other than their lips. For some reason these women thought it was Biblical to kiss on the lips but sinful to kiss other areas of the body. Ask yourself these questions. Is it right to kiss the ears, the neck, the breast, the arm, the abdomen and the thigh?

As I have pointed out I find no limitations on the type or manner of foreplay for a man and his wife.

I have three questions from the class last week I want to answer.

Question #1: "What causes or makes a person become a homosexual?"

Answer: This is a good question and one we want to know the answer in order that we may prevent our children from becoming homosexuals. Surely there are different reasons for different individuals but investigations have found certain situations that are conducive to the making of homosexuals. Most have found that the male homosexual is the result of a boy being reared too closely to females—mothers, sisters, aunts or grandmothers. He becomes so closely identified with females that he is not able to have a sexual outlet with a female but seeks release with another male. This same situation often is the reverse in females.

Question #2: "Can you identify homosexuals by their actions or by their dress?"

Answer: There are a few homosexuals, males and females, who can be recognized by their speech, mannerisms, and dress; but by and large only a small percentage can be recognized as such by the average person, though they are able to recognize one another.

Question #3: "How are individuals introduced to homosexuality?"

Answer: Not all are introduced in the same manner. Some are introduced by experimentation. For example, a number of years ago the mother of one of my teenage patients came in for advice. Her teenage daughter and one of her friends had gotten to the point that they wanted to spend the nights with one another with increased frequency. This disturbed the mothers. They decided to check on the girls and fixed the door to the bedroom so it could not be locked. When they heard suspicious noises they opened the door and caught the girls engaging in a homosexual act. I talked to the daughter of my patient. I found that in sleeping together these girls had began to fondle one another's breasts. They enjoyed this and

100

progressed until they were engaging in the usual lesbian acts. Because of this and other emotional problems of the girl, I referred her to a psychiatrist. This occurred many years ago. She has since married and has three children. I wish I could say that she had no further problems but I can't be sure since recently I heard she is divorced and is still in need of psychiatric help though not receiving it.

A second way children in particular are introduced to homosexuality is by being paid or enticed to participate by older homosexuals.

In conclusion to these teachings on homosexuality let me say that since it is a sin condemned in the Bible, let us recognize the problem, study the problem and do what we can to prevent this sin from becoming more prevalent.

CHAPTER 14

Masturbation

I WANT to discuss masturbation. By this I mean stimulation of the genital organs to orgasm achieved by manual or other bodily contact exclusive of sexual intercourse. Remember our definition of homosexuality was the exhibiting of sexual desire toward a member of one's own sex. So unless the masturbation was done by or to one of the same sex it would not be homosexual.

If a teenager masturbates or a man masturbates or a woman masturbates, it is not a homosexual act. It is however a method of individual sexual release. If you study the Scriptures, and I think in the past number of weeks we have read every Scripture concerning sexual acts in the Bible, and we have not found one Scripture in which masturbation is condemned. I dare say that none of you has been able to find where masturbation is condemned in the Bible. Yet we have found every sinful sexual act has been enumerated and condemned.

We found that if a man has relations with any woman not his wife or with any animal or man he is sinning. We found that if a woman has relations with any man not her husband or with any animal or woman she sins. The Bible is silent on masturbation. It is not condemned.

I know the frequency with which an act is done in no way makes it right or wrong but to allay the guilt of some in my audience let me say that Kinsey found that fifty-eight percent of the females and ninety-two percent of the males in his samples had masturbated to orgasm.[1]

To further allay the Christian's fears consider the following:

a. Masturbation is the one sexual outlet the teenager and the adult Christian has outside of marriage that is not condemned.

b. Masturbation is a socially accepted outlet, is it not?

---

[1] *Sexual Behavior in the Human Female.* 1953, Alfred C. Kinsey, Wendell P. Pomeroy, Clyde E. Martin and Paul H. Gebhardt. Chapter 5, pp. 132-190.

c. Masturbation harms no one, no, not the individual nor anyone else.

d. Masturbation produces no ill effects nor does it produce any of the side effects with which parents and grandparents have frightened childern for centuries. It does not cause a person to go crazy. It does not cause acne.

e. Masturbation for sexual release is preferable to fornication.

f. Masturbation does not spread disease.

g. Masturbation is normal unless it is engaged in to excess and to the neglect of other normal activities and pursuits. It does produce problems at times in the teenage school boy who becomes so obsessed with masturbation that he does it in the classroom and other public places.

h. As for masturbation in adults the same things apply as noted above. It is, I think, a scriptural sexual outlet.

i. There may be a need for masturbation in the married. Perhaps there is a prolonged illness of a mate. Masturbation in the well partner who is suddenly deprived of the usual outlet may be the one way to avoid falling into the temptation to commit adultery. Men in their forties, fifties and sixties who are suddenly deprived of a sexual outlet may cease to be able to perform when their wives recover. In these cases masturbation can have a prophylactic benefit. I have counseled with men whose wives would not engage in sexual relations, who would not follow the injunction we find in I Corinthians 7, that of rendering to their mates their conjugal rights. If a woman will not have relations with her husband, he has no other outlet. Many men have such strong sex drives that they have difficulty in sublimating them. Masturbation is by far better than to yield to temptation and to commit adultery.

I think I will finish my thoughts on masturbation by answering some questions that have been handed me since I announced that I would talk on this subject.

Question #1: "What is the difference between a person who commits fornication and one who masturbates?"

Answer: A fornicator is a sinner. Fornication has always been a sin for every man and every woman. I do not think you can equate fornication with masturbation. We have found no scripture condemning masturbation as we do fornication. Masturbation involves only one person, fornication requires two.

103

Question #2: "Would you consider a person to be a virgin who practices masturbation?"

Answer: A virgin is a person who has not had sexual intercourse. Therefore, even though a person has or continues to masturbate I would consider him or her a virgin.

Question #3: "What are wet dreams?"

Answer: Wet dreams or nocturnal emissions are spontaneous ejaculations by the male while he is asleep. They are usually preceded by or accompanied by a dream. Males are sexually stimulated every day, in many places and in many ways. These stimulations cause secretion of semen that is stored in the seminal vesicles. If there is no sexual outlet, if the male does not have intercourse, if he does not masturbate, sooner or later the pressure and engorgement reaches a point where there is spontaneous release while asleep. It has been maintained by some that this is the normal method of release and that masturbation for relief is wrong. I think those who maintain this do not realize how strong the sex drive is in some males. They do not know how uncomfortable some are when they need relief. Many males though intensely stimulated do not readily have nocturnal emissions. As a word of caution, do not gauge everyone's sex drive by your own. Realize there are wide variations in sex drives. Paul recognized this I think when he said, "If they cannot contain, let them marry: for it is better to marry than to burn" (I Corinthians 7:9).

In summarizing let me say that I think masturbation is an acceptable sexual outlet that violates no scripture that I can find and let me warn you not to teach your children anything concerning masturbation or any other matter concerning sex that you cannot find a scriptural basis for your belief and teaching.

CHAPTER 15

Birth Control and the Bible

THE BIBLE does not mention contraception or birth control. Yet we know it was practiced from the story found in Genesis 38:7-8. "And Judah said unto Onan, Go unto thy brother's wife, and marry her, and raise up seed to thy brother. And Onan knew that the seed should not be his; and it came to pass when he went in unto his brother's wife, that he spilled it on the ground, lest he should give seed to his brother." Remember under the old law the brother of the widow was commanded to take his brother's wife and "perform the duty of an husband's brother unto her" (Deuteronomy 25:5).

We found in the first passage that Judah told Onan to go into his brother's wife and raise up unto his brother seed. Onan knew the seed would not be his. So when he went in unto his brother's wife, instead of attempting to impregnate her, he spilled his seed upon the ground, "lest he should give seed to his brother." This is the act that displeased the Lord. He refused to obey the command to give seed to his brother,.

From this passage we learn that birth control was practiced. God was displeased because his command was broken. I have been unable to find any scripture which condemns birth control. I most certainly do not believe this passage teaches against the practice.

As I understand it, Roman Catholics for years used this as one of the proof texts to teach that birth control is contrary to the will of the Lord.

In I Corinthians 7:3-5 RSV we read: "The husband should give to his wife her conjugal rights, and likewise the wife to her husband, For the wife does not rule over her own body, but the husband does; likewise the husband does not rule over his body but the wife does. Do not refuse one another except perhaps by agreement for a season, that you may devote yourselves to prayer but then come together again, lest Satan tempt you through lack of control."

From this passage we know that marriage sanctifies intercourse.

Intercourse in marriage is right. The Lord recognized that if a man and woman were living together and did not have regular and frequent intercourse they would be tempted by Satan to seek satisfaction elsewhere.

I would expect the Bible would expressly prohibit contraception by withdrawal if the Lord considered it sinful. This is not what we find in the Scriptures. What we do read in Leviticus 15:16-18 is:

"And if any man's seed of copulation go out from him, then he shall wash all his flesh in water and be unclean until even. And every garment, and every skin, whereon is the seed of copulation, shall be washed in water, and shall be unclean until the even. The woman also with whom man shall lie with seed of copulation, they shall both bathe themselves in water, and be unclean until the even."

Here we find the emission of semen apart from coitus was not regarded as a sinful act. This is the same as withdrawal as a method of contraception. We know this because no sacrifice was demanded. The law of cleansing was a ceremonial thing.

However, if we turn to Levicitus 20:10-20 we read of numerous sexual crimes most of which were punishable by death. Every one of them involved intercourse apart from marriage. Once again we find no reference to withdrawal as a sin or sexual abuse.

Looking at these together we find withdrawal was not a sin because no sacrifice was demanded and no punishment was meted out for it. Since this was true it was permissible to use withdrawal as one method of birth control.

Since it was permissible under the law for man to practice birth control, I believe that there need not always be the possibility of a child each time a man has intercourse with his wife.

The Roman church considers conjugal love noble and teaches that the husband and wife do well to consider environment when planning children, but have relations only when there is a possibility of impregnation. For years it has tolerated and practiced the "unreliable rhythm system" as the only moral means of contraception. Catholics teach that the unreliabiilty is what makes it acceptable since "each and every marriage act must remain open to the transmission of life."

Let us look at the reasons it is unreliable. First, ovulation or shedding of the egg, is calculated backwards from the next menstural. Second, many get confused about the calculation. Third, there is a difference in the survival times of both the sperm and the eggs. Fourth, a woman is sexually more excitable around the time of ovulation and this method deprives her and her husband of relations when they are apt to enjoy them the most.

The Jews used withdrawal as a method of contraception. The Catholics have taught use of the rhythm system. Both are poor methods. If it is not a sin to use one, why not find a safer, more predictable, more satisfactory method.

You women know it is impossible to predict with absolute accuracy when your next menstrual period will begin. Because of this the women who use this method frequently get pregnant. This has produced many complaints and problems in the Catholic church, for example: I have had Catholic women who did not want another pregnancy and had requested reliable contraceptive advice and prescription. When they have used these other methods they have been guilt-ridden and have stopped attending confessionals and worship services of the church.

Newspapers and periodicals have had many articles from prominent Catholics, who have spoken out against the teachings of the church concerning contraception. The Catholic Church itself has not been as voracious in speaking out on contraception as in the past. As I understand it, they now are teaching that the Pope has not changed his position in spite of attacks. They explain that he was not speaking "Ex Cathedra." This gives them an out because then his statements are only his opinions.

I might also point out that they no longer push the teaching that the sin of Onan was against birth control. These teachings are still in their books but are left dormant.

In rebuttal to the statement that intercourse should always be accompanied by the possibility of creating life, what about the woman who has had a hysterectomy? What about the post-menopausal woman? What about the pregnant woman? What about the woman who knows her husband is sterile? Should these couples quit having relations? Should they be deprived of the pleasures of intercourse? If they should, then they would be disobeying I Corinthians 7:3-5 which we discussed previously in this lesson. We see then that the Roman church is not consistent in its teaching. I feel that if you are not consistent in your teachings and interpretation of the Bible you should re-examine your teachings and determine wherein you are erring.

Remember God created man with reason, judgment, sense of responsibility and a will. Reason and judgment is given so that he can decide his own destiny. Responsibility to himself, to his family and to his God is part of his duty. A will to follow or disobey God is his choice.

An animal is governed by instinct, not so with a man.

A man should be able to take his environment, take the Scriptures, interpret the Scriptures and apply the teachings of the Scriptures to his appetites (drives) and determine how they should be fulfilled in harmony with the Scriptures.

God said in Genesis 1:28, "Be fruitful and multiply." I count this a blessing as well as a command. Man is blessed when there are children in the home. It is a blessing to have the company and love of children. Note, God did not say, "Be fruitful, and multiply, and have two children, three children or ten children." I think it is left up to man how many children to have since God did not specify.

Remember marriage was instituted by God. Woman was created because it was "not good that the man should be alone" (Genesis 2:18). God created "a helper fit for him" (Genesis 2:18). Solomon said in Ecclesiastes 9:9, "Live joyfully with the wife whom thou lovest." When we make a scriptural application, we must think of all other Scriptures that apply. Marriage has always had a procreation function but no where do the Scriptures restrict sexual relations to the sole purpose of having children.

Another function of sexual relations in marriage apart from procreation is that of "moral prophylaxis."

I Corinthians 7:5,9 says, "Defraud ye not one the other except it be with consent for a time, that ye may give yourselves to fasting and prayer; and come together again, that Satan tempt you not for your incontinency." . . . "But if they cannot contain, let them marry; for it is better to marry than to burn."

We know that marriage is always to precede intercourse. Therefore, fornication, adultery and prostitution with or without

108

contraception is not a Christian option.

Sharing and meeting each others sexual needs is so important in marriage that Paul in I Corinthians 7:3-5 RSV advises against prolonged abstinence.

"The husband should give to his wife, and likewise the wife to her husband. For the wife does not rule over her own body, but the husband does; likewise the husband does not rule over his own body, but the wife does. Do not refuse one another except perhaps by agreement for a season, that you may devote yourself to prayer, but then come together again, lest Satan tempt you through lack of self-control."

He implies that frequent sexual relations are normal in marriage without mention of procreation.

Nowhere do the Scriptures teach that intercourse may not be engaged in primarily for mutual pleasure and mutual satisfaction. I re-emphasize this because many have taught that intercourse is only for the bearing of children. I ask what about the postmenopausal and the hysterectomized woman? Can they not have relations? Remember Sarah was past the menopause and she and Abraham were still having relations because Sarah did get pregnant and bore Isaac.

God has always provided a physical attraction and it is in the marriage relationhip where this is fulfilled. Intercourse is to be praised and not shunned. We have found from the Scriptures that sexual union had other functions than procreation such as:

a. conjugal rights of the wife
b. conjugal rights of the husband
c. to avoid temptation
d. for man to live joyfully with his wife (Ecclesiastes 9:9)
e. as a moral prophylaxis
f. to meet the emotional and sexual needs of the partner
g. mutual pleasure
h. mutual satisfaction.

Since there are other reasons for intercourse besides procreation how can conception be hindered in order that these other functions may be fulfilled or enhanced?

For this these reasons I believe the Christian has the right, yea sometimes even the obligation to practice birth control.

CHAPTER 16

Birth Control—Why and How

THERE ARE many factors that must be considered if you do not practice birth control or contraception.

A. Can you meet the physical, spiritual, economic and emotional needs of another child? If you are married, before you plan another child, sit down together and decide if you can meet the child's requirements of all the above needs.

B. Will another child affect the emotional or physical well-being of the father, the mother or other siblings? The entire time of the parents may be occupied caring for a deformed, crippled or retarded child and the parents may not have time to care for another child. Perhaps the mother or father is an emotional cripple and cannot care for another child even if the child is a normal child.

C. Overproduction of children is as sinful as selfish avoidance of parenthood. This is clearly shown in those over-populated countries such as India and China.

D. There may be economic reasons why another child is ill-advised. Perhaps a family cannot support another child. I Timothy 5:8 says, "But if any provide not for his own house, he has denied the faith and is worse than an infidel." All can think of a time when it would be right to limit a family. Take the father of two children who is disabled by injury or disease. Should he and his wife continue to have children?

E. Does either or both partners desire to remain childless? Why bring a child into a relationship where it is not wanted?

F. What should be done when there is a good chance of a genetically transmitted illness or deformity? The list of known congenital diseases and deformities is great and is increasing continuously. Is it good to take such chances with your offspring?

The above list is not complete but does point out some of the questions to be answered, some of the problems to be considered and some of the reasons why birth control should be offered, taught and practiced.

We found that birth control was practiced in Bible times. We could find no hint that its practice was condemned. Since it was practiced and not condemned, I think it is safe and right for us to practice and teach it, provided the motive is proper and, provided it is in the bond of matrimony. Since only the man and his wife are to pratcice birth control, I think it should be up to them to decide the methods they intend to use. I do not think the method is of any real significance as long as "whatsoever you do, do all to the glory of God" (I Corinthians 10:31).

I want to now discuss the various methods of contraception. When birth control is mentioned, many of you think only of the method you practice or may have heard discussed. Remember it is best to use the method that is most ideally suited at the time for each particular man and wife.

The most effective method of birth control is total abstinence. This method is in violation of I Corinthians 7. It promotes sin. It is immoral and a sin if not completely and absolutely agreeable to both parents.

The second method is coitus interruptus (withdrawal prior to ejaculation). It is unsatisfactory because intercourse is really not completed, thus it is frustating often to both partners. It is unreliable and unsafe as a measure of prevention of pregnancy because there is a high rate of pregnancies with this method. Pregnancies occur because there are often sperm in the penile secretion that occurs during foreplay and during intercourse prior to withdrawal. Frequently the male is not able to control the ejaculate and does not withdraw prior to ejaculation. Remember it takes only one sperm to fertilize the egg.

The third method is sterilization. This is permanent, but I think the same moral principles that apply to any method of contraception applies here. In the male, sterilization is a relatively simple office procedure done under local anesthesia. It requires no time loss from work. It is positive, permanent and can be checked by post-operative sperm counts to determine when the man is indeed sterile.

Sterilization of the female carries more risk and involves more expense. It requires hospitalization, general anesthesia, and opening of the abdominal cavity with its dangers of infection and adhesions. With adhesions, scarring of the abdominal organs, there is the possibility of future problems of bowel obstructions. Even though these possibilities exist, they are small and sterilization of the female is an acceptable, satisfactory, permanent method of birth control.

I might mention that in the last legislature of Tennessee, a bill was passed as one item in the Omnibus Bill that has made it legal for any physician in Tennessee to sterilize any male or female, married or single, eighteen years of age or over who presents themself and requests sterilization. The married do not have to have the consent of their spouse. This was a change in the law. I know of no physician who does not have his own criteria for sterilization. Our hospital by-laws and hospital medical staff by-laws have not been changed. There are still much stricter criteria that must be met. Since this law is now on the books, I believe it will have an effect on sterilizations being done on younger and younger individuals. When only one member of the marriage does not want children, sterilization can be done without the knowledge of the mate, since consent and permit of the spouse is not necessary.

We have discussed abstinence, coitus interruptus (withdrawal prior to ejaculation) and sterilization as two temporary and one permanent method of sterilization. I want now to discuss the many temporary methods of contraception practiced by most married partners. Some methods are more satisfactory than others. They can be classified under four general classes:

a. mechanical
b. chemical
c. physiological
d. combination of the above

Under mechanical methods there is the non-obstructive method which consists of the woman immediately douching with water after intercourse. Some use a spermaticide in the douche water. Let me advise you that both of these are unsatisfactory. The rate at which sperm swim and are able to move in the vagina make it virtually impossible to get up and effectively douche before the sperm have time to enter the cervical canal. Remember each ejaculate contains upwards to 300 to 400 million sperm which are deposited at the cervical os (mouth). Does it not take pleasure from intercourse for the woman to have to get up and immediately douche? The addition of the spermaticide to the douche helps but very little because of the speed and location of the sperm.

Next we come to the mechanical obstructive methods used by males. They are called rubber condoms or sheep gut sheaths. They can be purchased in many public restrooms, service stations and drug stores. From the places where they enjoy their greatest sale one recognizes that these are most often used for pre-marital and extra-marital relations. The effectiveness of condoms and sheaths is between ninety and ninety-eight percent. If the effectiveness were ninety-five percent then there is one chance in twenty of impregnation if intercourse occurs when the egg is present. With twenty-four days per month for a couple to have intercourse, it figures about one pregnancy every two to three years if only condoms or sheaths are used. This is about the pregnancy rate among fertile couples who use these alone. As a method of birth control they are unsatisfactory. Some condoms and sheaths are packaged in spermaticidal liquids, jellies, creams and powders. Each of these make their use a little more effective but each has its attendant problems. I have seen both men and women who have developed allergies, irritations and excoriations from all of these. All have had or seen an acute contact dermatitis of which posion ivy is probably the best known. These are the type of reactions I have seen on the penis, in the vagina and on the labia. The failures and the above-mentioned reactions however are not the chief complaints with the use of condoms and sheaths. These complaints are the loss of direct contact of the penis with the clitoris, labia and vagina, the diminished sensation of both partners, failure of the female to feel the ejaculation, the direct irritation of introitus and difficulty of intromission.

Another time-honored and much used mechanical obstructive method is the diaphragm which is a round ring with a rubber dome that is used by the female. It is placed in the vagina so that it mechanically blocks the entrance of sperm into the cervical canal. Diaphragms are used in conjunction with jellies and creams which contain a spermaticide. Therefore, the jellies and creams serve as both mechanical and chemical deterrents to the sperm. Diaphragms have the following disadvantages. They must be fitted and fitted correctly by a physician. They cannot be fitted correctly in a virgin without tearing or

113

stretching her hymeneal ring. They must be checked in place from time to time because the length and vault of the vagina changes. They must be inserted correctly each time by the woman who cannot always determine if it is correctly placed. The diaphragm itself must be checked regularly by the woman to make sure it has not developed defects. It must be kept clean. It must always be available wherever needed. Often it is not inserted ahead of time so at a point of intense sexual stimulation, foreplay must be interrupted, the diaphragm located, prepared and inserted. The same disadvantages that we discussed concerning jellies and cream sensitivities, allergies and irritation in conjunction with condoms are applicable with the diaphragm and these agents.

Another mechanical non-obstructive method of birth control is the intra-uterine device, the IUD as it is called. From the articles I have seen in many magazines this is presented as a relative new contraceptive. It really is not a new method. Ancient Egyptian camel drivers used the same method 2500 years ago to keep their camels from getting pregnant. Before the journey they would insert an apricot seed into the uterine cavity of their camels. The method is old. The device is new.

About fifty years ago the Germans introduced silver and gold intra-uterine devices. Because the silver and gold provoked little tissue reaction, they functioned quite adequately but these had their drawbacks. Chief among these was the rigidity of the metal, which damaged vessels and produced bleeding and the expulsion and cramping rates were high.

Since World War II with the improvements in plastics there has been put on the American and world markets scores of different IUDs. They are simple in design and insertion and are quite effective but are not 100 per cent effective. They are about ninety-seven per cent effective.

A three per cent failure rate is quite acceptable if your goal is to cut down on the birth rate of a country. It has been quite satisfactory in India where over-population is so great. In that country public health physicians go out into the neighborhoods, set up clinics and pay the women to have an IUD inserted. Even with a three per cent failure rate this is an effective method of lowering the birth rate.

Some of the problems encountered with the IUD besides

114

failures are as follows. The device is often expelled without the woman knowing it. The uterus often lets the woman know it is trying to expel the device by the cramping she has. Excessive menstrual bleeding and inter-menstrual bleeding is frequently seen. I have had to remove three devices because of endometritis (inflammation of the wall of the uterus) manifested by high fevers, chills and pain. Perforation of the uterus occurs. It is possible for the woman to get pregnant with an IUD in place and deliver the IUD at the time of delivery of a full term normal baby. However, often the IUD will cause a first or second trimester abortion or seventh month premature labor.

Do not let what I have said frighten those of you who have an IUD. They are satisfactory for many and if you have had your IUD in place three months without problems then in all likelihood you will have none. Continue to trust it and take the advice of your physician.

Before I leave this method, let me say one of the major causes of failure is the failure of the woman to check to make sure she has not expelled and lost her IUD. There is attached to the IUD a small nylon cord that protrudes from the cervix into the upper portion of the vaginal cavity. A woman can be certain of the presence of the IUD by inserting a finger into the vagina and feeling the cord. She should check this monthly about the tenth day of her menstrual cycle to be sure of its place prior to her ovulation time.

Until recently IUDs were not satisfactory for the woman who had never borne a child but newer devices are now available that are satisfactory. The problem in the nullipara is her uterine cavity is small and cramping and expulsion is a great problem.

On the other hand the grand multipara, the woman who has had five or more children, has had her uterus and cervix dilated so many times that the expulsion or slipping out rate is too high to be acceptable.

The next method of birth control I want to mention is the chemical method only. We discussed chemical methods in conjunction with three of the different types of mechanical methods but we frequently use chemicals as the primary and sole contraceptive. The vehicle for the chemical may serve as some mechanical blocker. I speak of the contraceptive jellies,

115

creams, foams and suppositories.

These are quite effective with failure rates between one and one and one-half percent. The problems with these products are the development of sensitivities and allergies by the woman and her husband to the ingredients. The high rate of allergies is due to the fact that they contain numerous organic and organic mercurial compounds which have a high index of sensitization.

Another class of birth control methods is the use of physiological agents. Physiological means appropriate to an organism's healthy or normal functioning.

It turns out that the use of physiological methods of birth control is the most effective method that is practical. Basically this method works by prevention of ovulation by hormones. This is accomplished by cyclic administration of synthetic estrogen and a synthetic progesterone. If ovulation is prevented, then this method should be one hundred percent effective. This is not entirely true because of forgetting to take the pill and because of rare physiological failure. The effectiveness of the pill is above ninety-nine per cent plus effective in every study I have seen. Another proof of the effectiveness of the pill is current drop in the birth rate. Besides effectiveness, the beautiful part is the ease of taking the pill.

There is much fear concerning the pill, much of which has been generated by scare articles in women's magazines designed to sell magazines. In reality these hormones were in use in 1949 and 1950 when I was in medical school. They were used then and have continued to be used to regulate and control menses. However, we used to use dosages in the fifteen to twenty milligrams per day range. The dosage today in use as birth control pills is in the one to two milligram per day range. After twenty-five years of usage the side effects are well known. Their advantages far outweigh their disadvantages.

There are various pills on the market with different modes of administration.

One method is a twenty or twenty-one pill pack. All pills are alike. The woman takes a pill for twenty or twenty-one days straight beginning on the fifth day of her period. She stops and when her menses begins she restarts her pills on the fifth day.

Another method is the use of a twenty-one pill cycle. Once

116

again the first cycle of pills is started on the fifth day of the menses. The pills are then taken for twenty-one days, omitted for seven days and the cycle repeated. With this method the woman always begins taking her pills the same day of the week every four weeks. The menses occurs during the week she is off the pills.

There is another method of administration which is almost the same. These packets of pills have twenty-one active pills and either seven placebo pills or seven iron pills for the prevention of anemia. After starting the first cycle on the fifth day of the menses the pills are taken continuously, the menses occurring during the seven days the placebo or iron pills are being taken.

The sequential method is another way the pill is given. The first sixteen tablets are the same, the last five contain an additional progestational agent to mimic the females own rise of this substance the latter portion of the cycle. They are administered the same as the others and come designed to be omitted until the fifth day of the menses, or for one week. Some have seven placebos or seven iron tablets taken at the end of the hormonal tablets. These are taken continuously once the cycle is started.

Every company that manufactures or distributes these pills has developed a package designed to assist the woman in keeping up with her dosage. Most of us who prescribe the pill recommend it to be taken at bedtime each night. Taken at bedtime there are fewer forgotten pills. Also if the pills produce some nausea as it does in some women, the nausea occurs while they are asleep. Before discussing the side effects and drawbacks of the pill let me mention the other physiological methods used by the female.

There are physiological methods for the woman who does not want to take the pill. She can get monthly injections at her physician's office. The dosage is difficult to calculate and frequently the woman may go up to seven or eight months without a menstrual period.

Another method for the woman who does not want to take the pill is the insertion of a vaginal ring into the vagina on the fifth day of the cycle, leave it for twenty-one days and then remove it. The woman absorbs the hormones that are impregnated into the ring. The woman is making use of the same

117

hormones as the woman who takes the pill.

Another method of prevention of ovulation as a method of birth control is the implantation of a hormone pellet under the skin through a surgical incision. The pill is slowly absorbed and ovulation can be prevented over a long period of time. The disadvantages of this method is that it requires surgery, absorption is variable, the menses are delayed usually until almost complete absorption, and pregnancy is possible before the patient is aware that she is in need of another implantation.

The most important benefit of the pill is that it is virtually 100 percent effective. When taken as directed, the failure rate is well below one percent.

I think that birth control pills have had a great amount of unjust criticism. If a woman is on the pill and develops some symptom or illness that is not readily recognizable, then the pill is blamed. If it is a toxic reaction, many do not think to question all the other medications the woman may be taking. Many take those prescribed for by her several physicians. These women take medicines from three or four physicians each of whom are unknown by the others. Friends, neighbors, relatives and fellow office workers contribute their pills for the relief of many symptoms. The woman may be in contact with several garden sprays, insecticides, and herbicides, not counting the household chemicals, detergents, cosmetics, hair bleaches, hair dyes, conditioners, straighteners and such like. Remember also, almost every food stuff purchased is possible suspect for poisons from spraying, plus those substances used to preserve them.

What gets the blame? Why the pill of course. What else? So the first thing done is the woman is taken from the pill and tells everyone about her bad experience.

If you ask, "What about thrombophlebitis?" Yes, there is an increase in thrombophlebitis, with its morbidity and its mortality, but the risk of pregnancy is greater than the risk of thrombophlebitis by a wide margin. Remember pregnancy carries a risk. Remember the women who miscarry and hemorrhage. Remember the infections of pregnancy. Remember the mortality of Caesarean section necessitated by bleeding from a low placental implantation (placenta praevia), premature placental separation (abruptio placenta), abnormal presenta-

118

tion or a fetus too large for pelvic delivery (cephalo-pelvic disproportion).

All things considered the taking of the pill is safer than a pregnancy. If you are dealing with a woman who has a mortal fear of pregnancy or a woman who will become psychotic if another pregnancy occurs, you are dealing with something that cannot be reduced to a statistic.

Let us discuss the common side effects of the pill. No one will deny that they do occur. I believe there are some side effects to every medication. I have many patients who cannot take aspirin, codeine, penicillin and every medicine I prescribe. Just because one patient cannot take a medicine I do not quit using it. I weigh each patient's case individually and prescribe to the best of my ability.

If a woman has a history of having had thrombophlebitis, phlebothrombosis or has more than negligible varicose veins, then I will prescribe another method of contraception. If a woman who is on the pill develops thrombophlebitis (an inflammed vein with a clot) or any evidence of stasis or venous blockage, I will immediately take her off the pill and treat the condition vigorously. Women who are on the pill may be better protected than those not on the pill because they are under a physician's care. They must be to continue to receive the pills. They are aware of the problems because of instructions they have been given. They report any new symptoms. In fact they seek medical advice earlier than their counterparts who are not on the pill. Consequently minor problems come under the physician's scrutiny earlier in their course than they would otherwise.

Some women complain of headaches while on the pill. On the other hand many women have headaches and are not taking the pill. Take them off the pill for a month. If the headaches stop during the time the patient is not taking the pill and if they reoccur when the pill is restarted, I will agree that the pill is possibly the cause. A physician has a couple of alternatives; one is to prescribe another method of contraception, another is to change the pill to one containing different hormone dosages or different ratios of hormone dosage.

For the woman who complains of excessive weight gain while on the pill, I can only answer if a woman eats more than

119

her body uses she gains weight, if she eats less than she uses she loses weight. Remember also as women get older they have a tendency to gain weight. Also remember, quite often a woman is put on the pill after a pregnancy and delivery. Ladies, remember how often there is weight gain at this time of your life.

Water retention is a frequent complaint that is easy to control by reducing the sodium intake and/or giving the woman a diuretic.

As with all medications there may be a true allergy which requires stopping the pills and instituting the appropriate treatment.

Occasionally breakthrough bleeding occurs as a complication. This is handled by doubling up on the pills for one or two days. If this reoccurs repeatedly, then change the pills to another brand.

The most frequent serious problem with the pill is human error. The woman forgets to take one or two pills. She gets breakthrough bleeding or gets pregnant. The packets in which the pills are packed are so made and labeled to remind the woman if she forgets a pill. Most of the pills are potent enough that the missing of one tablet will not result in a failure. If you are in the habit of taking your pills at bedtime and discover one morning you forgot to take your pill the night before, take it when you discover your mistake.

You may be wondering, "Why don't they have a pill for the male?" There is such a pill perfected. The problem is to get the male to take them. Males are not motivated because they are not going to get pregnant.

There is also available for males injections but they will not go in for injections. The pills and the injections for males work on the principle that they pervent the maturation of sperm.

Another method available for males is implantation of pellets of hormones to do the same thing. If you could get the male to go in for the surgical implantation of a pellet, you could persuade him to have a vasectomy.

I think you might be interested in a new group of organic chemical compounds called prostaglins that have been isolated. The hope is that when perfected a woman can take one pill each month at the time her menstrual period is due. They produce a shedding of the lining of the uterus. There has been much

120

written in the newspaper lately concerning the prostaglins because they offer great promise. The big drawback of those available are the side effects. Besides producing a shedding of the uterine lining, they produce uncontrollable movements of the bowels and the urinary bladder as well as nausea and vomiting.

You can readily see the advantage of this kind of birth control measure. It can be taken after exposure. A woman will only have to remember one pill every twenty-eight days. If she wants to finish her period before a trip or a vacation she needs only to take the prostaglin pill soon enough ahead of time so that she can finish her period prior to her trip.

I feel that in time the undesirable side effects of the prostaglins will be eliminated.

The comments in this lesson are to give the advantages and disadvantages of the various available birth control methods. Let your physician, obstetrician or gynecologist prescribe for you after taking a history and examining you. This is the only way *you* can be sure of having the best birth control method.

ADDENDUM: In May, 1973, the Federal Drug Administration approved the use of diethylstilbesterol as a method of contraception in those cases where intercourse has already occurred in which pregnancy is undesired or contraindicated. It must be given within twenty-four hours after exposure in dosages of twenty-five milligrams two times daily for five days. The drawback of this therapy is that in this dosage range nausea and vomiting are almost invariably a problem.

121

CHAPTER 17

Mandrakes

MY TOPIC is mandrakes. Many of you may think a mandrake is a male duck, but if you remember the story of Rachel and the mandrake roots you will realize I am talking about an early story concerning a supposed fertility herb. The ancients thought that mandrake roots were useful in promoting fertility. A significant difference between them and the newer fertility drugs used now experimentally was that they did not produce multiple births.

Their benefit is difficult to evaluate but they apparently were of some help—the mechanism of which we will discuss later.

Mandrakes are called "May apples" and "devil's apples." It is a plant which grows about a foot high, has purple blooms in May, has a tubular root, and is akin to the potato family. The plant blooms with a purple flower in May which turns into a two-inch large apple. The roots of the plant and the fruit of the plant both have been used to promote fertility in the female.

The reference to mandrakes is found in Genesis 30:14.

"And Reuben went in the days of the wheat harvest, and found mandrakes in the field, and brought them unto his mother Leah. Then Rachel said to Leah, Give me, I pray thee, of thy son's mandrakes. And she said unto her, Is it a small matter that thou take away my son's mandrakes also? And Rachel said, Therefore he shall lie with thee tonight for thy son's mandrakes. And Jacob came out of the field in the evening, and Leah went to meet him, and said, Thou must come in unto me; for surely I have hired thee to night for thy son's mandrakes."

This story really began in the twenty-ninth chapter of Genesis. Remember the love story of Jacob and Rachel? How he covenanted with Laban for Rachel but was deceived with Leah. He had to work another seven years to marry Rachel. Remember Leah bore him Reuben, Simeon, Levi and Judah. Remember Rachel in her grief for her barrenness gave her handmaid

Bilah to Jacob and she bore him Dan and Napthali. Then Leah gave him her handmaid Zilpah who bore him Gad and Asher. It was recorded in the passage we quoted how Reuben found mandrakes with which Leah bought her husband of Rachael. Leah then bore him Issachar, Zebulun and Dinah.

Rachel's desire to have a child bordered on the psychotic. She "said unto Jacob, give me children or else I die" (Genesis 30:10). If not psychotic she was certainly irrational. We know anxiety, tension and worry will affect fertility. Perhaps the mandrakes Rachel obtained from Reuben and Leah served no purpose, however, it is interesting to me as a physician to think about it in the light of the following. Mandrake roots and "May apples" have been used throughout the ages as sedatives, soporifics and fertility potions. A nervous, tense, worried woman sometimes does not conceive. When the tension over being childless is relived by the adoption of a child, these women frequently conceive. Perhaps the sedative effect which the mandrakes had, helped Rachel conceive.

You may question my wisdom in even considering this possibility. But, daily for years I have prescribed medications. I have also prayed that my patients would benefit from my prescribing and that they would get well. I believe it is right to pray for the sick to get well but I also believe it is necessary that we do everything in our power to help the sick. Prayer alone is not the answer. Medicine and therapy without the help of God is useless. I believe God works through men and the actual physiology of the sick. God does not always, though he can, set aside the laws of nature. We pray for a certain thing to happen and God can cause it to happen through the routine laws of nature.

As an example I have seen many of my patients sick to the point of death, when all who saw them and all who were ministering to them thought death was imminent. Then after prayers had been made for the sick they began to improve. I believe, "the prayer of faith shall save the sick" (James 5:15). I do not count this a miracle but only that the Lord can intervene. He can permit the body to build its own defenses. He can cause deteriorating bodily functions to respond, that bacteria succumb to antibiotics, that anxieties be relieved, that the physicians become aware of new modalities of therapy, that mistakes in

123

therapy be recognized, and that any one of myriads of variables be changed only enough that the patient begin to respond and improve.

I do not believe we can rely on prayer alone. I certainly do not want to rely on my diagnosing and prescribing without the blessing of the Lord.

Whether the mandrakes were of benefit or not, I am not prepared to say. As a physician I find many Bible stories that have a different appeal and attraction to me because of my training as a physician.

CHAPTER 18

Circumcision

IN SOME of the child's first Sunday School lessons a child hears about circumcision. Many reach adulthood without ever knowing what the term means. I have learned this from talking with some of my female patients. Though married they do not know what circumcision is and frequently do not know whether or not their husbands have been circumcised. Wives should know if their husbands have been circumcised because there are medical conditions for which female patients require treatment in which the treatment is different if their consort is or is not circumcised.

Circumcision comes from two root words circum (around) and caedere (to cut). To circumcise a male is to cut off his prepuce or his foreskin.

God gave a covenant to Abraham in Genesis 17:10-14.

"This is my covenant, which ye shall keep, between me and you and thy seed after thee; every man child among you shall be circumcised. And ye shall be circumcised. And ye shall circumcise the flesh of your foreskin; and it shall be a token of the covenant betwixt me and you. And he that is eight days old shall be circumcised among you, every man child in your generations, he that is born in the house, or bought with money of any stranger, which is not of thy seed. He that is born in thy house, and he that is bought with thy money, must needs be circumcised: and my covenant shall be in your flesh for an everlasting covenant. And the uncircumcised manchild whose flesh of his foreskin is not circumcised, that soul shall be cut off from his people; he hath broken my covenant.

The seed of Abraham was to be circumcised on the eighth day. Any person bought or brought into the house was to be circumcised. This was a religious covenant yet it was an act that promoted cleanliness and helped prevent disease.

I think it wise for us to note that the physical requirements and the dietary restrictions the Lord placed on the Hebrews have all proven to be of benefit to man.

So it is with the man who has been circumcised. It is easier for him to keep himself clean. He is not infected as often, nor is he as likely to transmit disease. The Hebrews lived in a hot climate where germs grew rapidly. The foreskin which could not be retracted was an ideal place for germs to grow. The area is kept moist by the last two or three drops of urine that comes from the urethra after a male urinates. The smegma and desquamated skin serve as an ideal culture media.

I see men today who in their forties, fifties, even sixties who must be circumcised because chronic and recurrent acute infections of the foreskins develop intolerable problems.

There are other conditions circumcision has been found to be of benefit.

"According to a ten-city survey, the incidence of cancer of the cervix in American white women is 35.2 per 100,000, in American non-white women, the rate is 61.2 per 100,000. In Israeli women, the rate is 2.2 per 100,000 and this exceedingly low rate is matched by studies in Jewish women in the United States.[1]

Note there are seventeen times as many cancers of the cervix in white American females as among Israeli women and among the non-white Americans about thirty times as many. One thing that is different in these samples of females is that Israeli men are still practicing circumcision whereas many white non-Jewish men and far fewer non-white American males do not practice it.

In India where cancer of the cervix accounts for about forty percent of female malignancies we find one religious group in which it is rare. The difference is the Mohammadans practice circumcision, whereas the Hindus do not. We find this difference in cancer of the cervix rates holds true in all parts of the world where circumcision is practiced.

Another fact that we should note is that cancer of the head of the penis is almost unheard of among males who have been circumcised. Whereas, it is common in men who have not been circumcised, especially among men who engage in occupations in which there is chronic irritation of the foreskin and penile head such as in chimney sweepers and certain machinists who drench themselves in cutting oils.

[1] Search the Scriptures. A Physician Examines Medicine in the Bible. By Robert B. Greenblatt, A.B., M.D., C.M., p. 42.

In summary besides the prevention of disease and the transmission of disease, circumcision cuts down on cancer of the cervix in the consorts of the circumcised as well as cuts down on cancer of the head of the penis in the circumcised. We see then that circumcision is of benefit both to the man and his wife. I bring this up not to make a plea for universal circumcision but to show that there are definite benefits.

I am aware of the writings that have appeared in popular magazines recently stating that most circumcisions are unnecessary surgery. Personally, I think the benefits already mentioned are enough to warrant circumcising all males. However, aside from them is the fact that a long redundant foreskin even if it can be retracted for cleansing of the head of the penis is a source of an urinous odor and media for bacterial growth. This occurs because a male has great difficulty when he voids to empty all the urine from his urethra. When the penis is replaced, this urine emerges and is trapped beneath a large redundant foreskin.

The Hebrews were commanded to circumcise the male "on the eighth day." Today since we do not do this as a religious act we circumcise the infant on the first, second or third day so he will be able to leave the hospital with his mother. In our hospital a bleeding and a clotting time is done prior to circumcision to insure that the infant has no abnormal bleeding traits.

The circumcision is done without anesthesia. Complications are extremely rare.

In closing let me give one last advantage of young boys being circumcised that has nothing to do with cancer, disease or physical health. Since most boys are circumcised, the boy who is not circumcised is different. He is ridiculed by his classmates when he goes to the school restroom. This was brought to my attention when a mother brought a child to me to check because he wet his pants in school. Examination and urinalysis was negative. Upon further questioning I found that my young patient would not go to the school restroom because of the ridicule he received from his schoolmates. Sometimes he could not wait until school was out. Needless to say, a circumcision resulted in curing this boy.

CHAPTER 19

Venereal Disease

A VENEREAL DISEASE is a contagious disease that is typically acquired in sexual intercourse.

In the early 1950s the venereal disease rate in the United States reached its lowest point. This came about because of the extreme sensitivity of the gonoccus bacteria and the syphilis spirochete to penicillin. Syphilis was almost eradicated and gonorrhea was not a real health problem. However, with the Korean War and the return of veterans with resistant strains as well as an increase fluidity of the population, gonorrhea began to spread. Syphilis kept pace. With the advent of the Hippie movement in the 60s further impetus was given. Today in some of our cities gonorrhea is the most common communicable disease, surpassing the common cold and the childhood diseases.

People have lost their fear of these diseases. They do not seek treatment as they once did. Perhaps you have noticed the billboards along our highways and the newspaper ads advising the infected to seek help. Telephone numbers are listed which can be called where one can receive confidential advice concerning treatment. Early diagnosis with prompt treatment of the infected person plus treatment of all the contacts is required for control and eradication.

Let us consider each of the venereal diseases, beginning first with syphilis which is most serious in its consequences and second most freqeunt. It is caused by the syphilis spirochete, a slender spirally undulating bacteria. The primary lesion of spyhilis is a chancre or sore. It begins a little papule or raised area which becomes more indurated, the center of which breaks down and begins to drain. The spirochetes are in the drainage. The lesion most often is on the genital or anal area. The next most common site is on or about the lips. These sites indicate that the usual mode of transmission is intercourse though it can be spread by kissing. If syphilis is not suspected, it is not diagnosed. If it is not diagnosed, it is not treated. If it is not treated, the primary syphilitic chancre will heal spontaneously in two to three weeks and the infected person has no further symptoms until secondary syphilis erupts with a generalized rash and vague nondescript generalized symptoms. Without diagnosis and treatment secondary syphilis symptoms also subside after a few weeks.

The unsuspecting carrier may know nothing for years until he accidently is found to have a positive serology or develops symptoms from tertiary or late syphilis. These symptoms are so myriad that in the early nineteen hundreds there was a saying that if a physician knew all the manifestations of syphilis as well as the differential diagnosis then he knew medicine. Syphilis can mimic almost any disease. Syphilis attacks two main organ systems, the cardiovascular and the neurological. The most common lesions are syphilitic aortitis which causes dilation of the aorta with its complications, aortic valvular insufficiency, enlargement of the heart, heart failure or aortic rupture. The neurological lesions produce tabes dorsalis with its wasting, pain, incoordination of voluntary movements and reflexes, and disorders of sensation, nutrition and vision.

A person with secondary and tertiary syphilis is capable of transmitting to their offspring congenital syphilis. This is the reason every obstetrician obtains blood for a serological test for syphilis early in his care for a maternity case. This test is repeated upon admission to the hospital. In fact in our area all hospital admissions have serological tests for syphilis. The tests now used are more sensitive and more specific than the old Wasserman test that was so widely used.

Syphilis can be transmitted by casual contact even though I think well over ninety percent is transmitted by sexual contact. It can be transmitted by kissing, by handling of the sores and by transferring the spirochete from the chancre to an open lesion. Because of the ease of transmission and the seriousness of the disease, government agencies are spending a great amount of money trying to eradicate it. There are numerous pilot programs functioning attempting to find the best way. Numerous charity clinics are well-financed and well-advertised toward this end.

The second most feared venereal disease is the most common. This is gonorrhea, which is caused by the gonococcus bacteria. In a recent meeting of the American College of Gynecologists and Obstetricians, a physician from Detroit said in some parts of his city, gonorrhea was more common than the common cold. I do not know what type of practice he had but I assume he knew whereof he spoke. He went on to tell of the number of cases he was seeing and he discussed the difficulties he was having effecting a cure. Many of you cannot believe the problems that are in our large cities.

We live among a stable population. We live with our wives and husbands. We are faithful to our wives and husbands. These things are not true in large segments of our population in which there is promiscuity among teenagers, and among the married, with adultery and fornication in the form of wife-swapping and sex parties. It is no wonder we have an epidemic of gonorrhea in America.

One of the problems with gonorrhea is that it is getting more and more difficult to cure. In the 1940s 300,000 units of penicillin would cure over ninety-nine percent of cases of gonorrhea. Today the recommended dose in males is 2,400,000 units, for the female it is 4,800,000 units. Even at sixteen times the dosage level, the cure rate today with penicillin is around eighty percent.

From the time of contact until the appearance of symptoms in the male it is two to eight days. The symptoms in the male are burning, painful urination and a thick, yellow urethral discharge. The diagnosis is made by typical findings on a Gram stained smear or a culture. The female may be asymptomatic since the infection is usually vaginal and not urethral. The Gram Stain is less reliable as a diagnostic tool. The culture is better but not as good as in the male.

A question that is frequently asked is, "Can you get the gonorrhea from a toilet seat?" Let me answer by saying even though the urethral and vaginal secretions contain the gonococci bacteria, the bacteria die if the secretion drys. The possibilities of catching gonorrhea from door knobs, commode handles, toilet seats and such like, is extremely remote. I have found that if I go deep enough into the history and am persistent enough that a venereal contact can be found either for the patient or his or her consort.

There are other venereal diseases that we must be aware of these days because of their rising incidences. The first in granuloma inguinal which is a chronic pus producing lesion of the skin, lymphatics and lymph nodes usually seen around the anal and genital areas. The incubation period is eight to twelve weeks. It presents itself as a foul-smelling sore. This type formerly was found predominately in the black population because of their sensitivity to the infecting organism, but because the increase in population movement and the now frequent consorting of whites with blacks it is becoming prevalent among whites also. The diagnosis is made by finding organisms within cells called Donovan Bodies in smears or in biopsy specimens. Strict cleanliness is the main method of eradication and prevention of this disease. This disease responds to treatment with tetracycline and its analogues.

Another venereal disease is lymphogranuloma venerium. It is caused by a venereal virus. The incubation time is five to twenty-one days. The manifestations are tender swelling abscesses which open and drain spontaneously. These become secondarily infected and become foul-smelling. They occur around the rectum and vagina. They heal by scarring and produce vaginal and rectal strictures requiring surgery to treat these complications. In as much as lymphogranuloma venerium is caused by a virus and we have no effective antiviral treatment. This disease must run its course. Treatment consists of treating the complications.

Another venereal disease though less well known but still increasing is known as chancroid or soft chancre which is caused by a Gram negative staining organism, called Hemophylus Ducrey. It has an incubation of three to five days. Its symptoms are matted swollen tender inguinal lymph nodes. Our available antibiotics are quite effective in treating this disease.

There are two infections that may or may not be venereal in transmission.

Trichomoniasis is caused by trichomonads which are unicellar flagellates. They can be found in the flora of normal colons and in vaginal secretions of nonsymptomatic females. However, it has been shown that if trichomonads are found in a wife's secretions then they can be found in ninety percent of the husbands of such women. If they are found in a husband's urethra, then they can be demonstrated in ninety-five percent of the wives of these men. For many years it was difficult for phy-

131

sicians to eliminate this organism that produces irritation, discharge and itching. Recently however, a fairly specific medication, which if given to both husband and wife at the same time will effect a cure. This is one of the organisms that lives and thrives in the moist foreskin of the uncircumcised male. It is also much more difficult to cure the uncircumcised than it is the circumcised.

Candidiasis or moniliasis is a condition caused by candida albicans. This can also be or not be of venereal origin. Many of the women in my audience have been bothered with this infection, commonly known as thrush. I have seen this infection change in its response to treatment in the past twenty-five years. In the forties and fifties about the best treatment we had was gentian violet which turned everything it touched a blue purple. In the late fifties nystatin was found which proved effective in treating almost all monilial infections but in the past fifteen years the infections have become more and more resistant to treatment. Today Amphotericin-B is probably the most effective available treatment.

To sum up this lesson let me remind you that we are having an epidemic of venereal disease in the United States. Our methods of treatment are much less effective today than in the past.

CHAPTER 20

Eunuchs

I WOULD LIKE to discuss a passage in Matthew 19:12 where Christ teaches,

"For there were some eunuchs which were so born from their mother's womb: and there are some eunuchs, which are made eunuchs of men: and there be eunuchs which have made themselves eunuchs for the kingdom of heaven's sake. He that is able to receive it let him receive it."

Long ago before modern endocrinology Christ recognized that there were three types of eunuchs. A eunuch is a male castrate, a man who does not have the benefit of functioning testicles to secrete male hormones. It was hundreds of years later before scientists recognized what Christ taught in the first century.

Christ taught that some males were born without testicles and because of this defect they would always be eunuchs. He recognized that some were castrated before puberty and some were castrated by themselves or others after puberty. The important difference in these three types of eunuchs is their development, growth and sex drive.

I hope after this lesson when you read this passage it has a clearer meaning to you.

From antiquity men have known that a eunuch was good to guard harems and was good to be in charge of female servants because they had no sex drive and would not molest the women in the castle or harem. There was a trade among ancient orientals and Egyptians in the near and far east for congenital eunuchs and males castrated before puberty.

Some males are born without testicles. These males are congenital eunuchs. Some males have their testicles removed before puberty. These also are eunuchs and functionally are the same kind of eunuchs. They are deprived of male hormones and do not take on the secondary sexual characteristics of males. They always appear as a child in many ways. They do not develop beards nor do they develop the male body build. Instead, because of the production of estrogens, female hormones, secreted by the adrenal glands and not counter-balanced by male hormones, they take on female characteristics. The individuals develop breasts, larger hips, keep a high-pitched voice, develop a female distribution of hair and they do not develop a beard. The pubic hair distribution is female type in shape rather than male. These individuals in fact appear as females rather than males.

For a long period of time, even up until the last century, it was a known practice of some to remove the testicles of males prior to puberty to produce an individual with a high soprano voice who could sing in some of the well-renowned choirs.

"For several centuries, the choir boys of the Sistine Chapel in Rome were castrated in order to preserve their soprano voices; such singers became known as 'castrati.' Only in 1878, upon the accession of Pope Leo XIII, was the Italian practice of castrating boys in order to train them as adult soprano singers brought to an end."[1]

We are all familiar with the castration of animals. Castrate a male cow and you produce a steer that will be docile, will grow larger and will not walk over you or your fences.

Most of you have eaten capons. A capon is a castrated rooster. Besides making the rooster grow larger, fatter and have more delectable meat, the rooster develops personality changes. These changes are striking. The normal rooster crows, struts, fights with other roosters for domination, chases hens, and appears to show off his comb and wattles. Following caponization, he is docile, his comb and wattles shrink, his crowing stops, he loses his aggressiveness, and he not only plays with the hens but even poor male that he is, sets on their eggs.[2]

For a great number of years it has been known that a person deficient in thyroid could be successfully treated by giving thyroid from healthy normal animals. This is successful because active thyroid is stored in the normal thyroid gland.

Physician scientists attempted to give extracts from testicles

---

[1] *Search the Scriptures.* A Physician Examines Medicine in the Bible, by Robert B. Greenblatt, M.D., p. 58.
[2] *Ibid.,* p. 57.

to rejuvenate males whose own production of testosterone was waning. This was unsuccessful because the testicles do not store testosterone. However, synthetic testosterone has been commercially synthesized. Now there is a treatment for the eunuch. The vigorous treatment with testosterone will counteract the estrogenic effects on the eunuch and will produce the virilizing effects such as enlargement of the penis, male hair growth and a coarsening of the voice.

A male castrated before puberty does not develop the sex drive. On the other hand a male castrated after puberty has developed the sex drive and remembers this drive after castration. He is not able to perform as a male unless he is given testosterone sublingually or by intramuscular injections.

Castration has a place in the treatment of cancer of the prostate today. One of the standard methods of treatment of cancer of the prostate besides surgical removal of the primary tumor is to remove the testicles of the patient to stop the production of testosterone. This tumor is stimulated by testosterone. In addition, the patient is placed on estrogen usually in the form of diethylstilbesterone, which suppresses the growth of the tumor. These patients develop the secondary sex characteristics of females. Many men will not accept this form of treatment. It does not matter if a man does have cancer of the prostate, it is difficult to interest him in a bilateral-orchidectomy, the removal of both testicles, to prolong his life.

I shall never forget the first time I discussed this with a patient. I was in training and had been requested by the surgeon to talk to the patient, to explain the procedure and its side effects. Even though the patient was in his seventies, he refused to have his testicles removed. I asked him, "Why not?" Even though I knew he was not married, and they would be of no use to him if he died of cancer, his answer was, "But, Doctor, they dress me up so much." This was his argument for keeping them. I think it shows the reluctance of men to give up certain parts of their bodies just as some women refuse to sacrifice a breast for a malignancy of the breast.

Let me advise you not to make up your mind ahead of time about what treatment you will or will not accept. Wait until you have to make a decision then weigh all the facts. Then decide to accept the mode of treatment deemed best by your physician at that time.

I hope the next time you read Matthew 19:12 you will remember how far ahead of his time Christ was in the field of endocrinology.

CHAPTER 21

Abortions

IN MY discussion I use the word abortion to mean the surgical removal or the medical expulsion of a human fetus during the first twelve weeks of gestation. Many of you in my audience have had spontaneous abortions, termed miscarriages. To the physician all of these are abortions. They are either spontaneous, surgical or medical.

In preparation for our discussion let us read Leviticus 24:17, "And he that killeth any man shall be surely put to death." I quote this to show that murder under the Law was punishable by death. Note however in Exodus 21:22-25 we read, "If men strive, and hurt a woman with child, so that her fruit depart from her, and yet no mischief follow: he shall be surely punished, according as the woman's husband will lay upon him: and he shall pay as the judges determine. And if any mischief follow, then thou shalt give life for life, eye for eye, tooth for tooth, hand for hand, foot for foot, burning for burning, wound for wound, stripe for stripe." Here we find that if a man hurt a woman and caused her to abort he was not put to death. Since he was not, this indicates it was not considered murder. This was true as long as "no mischief followed" or as long as the woman did not die, but "if any mischief followed" or if the woman died then he was to "give life for life." This was the punishment for murder.

From this we can summarize. A murderer was put to death. A man who caused a woman to abort and lose her unborn child was not put to death. If the woman died, the man was to pay for her life with his life. I understand this to indicate that the unborn child was not a living soul since every time a murder was committed the death penalty followed.

Let us see if the Scriptures indicate when a living soul begins. Genesis 2:7 teaches, "And the Lord formed man of the dust of the ground, and breathed into his nostrils the breath of life; and man became a living soul." Man became a living soul when the Lord breathed into him the breath of life. Does the fetus

137

become a living soul before it receives the breath of life? I think not.

Let me anticipate your next question. Does the Bible not say, "The life is in the blood"? Let us read Leviticus 17:11. "For the life of the flesh is in the blood." Deuteronomy 12:23 commands, "Only be sure that thou eat not the blood; for the blood is the life." Genesis 7:17 tells us, "And they went in unto Noah into the ark, two and two of all flesh, wherein is the breath of life."

We have passages here that are not mutually exclusive. Two state the "life is in the blood," the others speak of the breath of life. I think we know that prior to the Lord putting breath of life into Adam he had a heart, he had a brain with vessels and these vessels and heart were filled with blood just as the vessels and the heart of the fetus are filled with blood. However, Adam did not become a living soul until after the Lord breathed into him the breath of life (Genesis 2:7). My opinion is that the fetus is not a living soul until it has the breath of life.

When the Lord was speaking to Noah, he used the same phrase to describe mankind in Genesis 6:17.

"And behold, I, even I, do bring a flood of waters upon the earth, to destroy all flesh, wherein is the breath of life, from under heaven; and every thing that is in the earth shall die."

You may ask, "Do you not have life when the sperm unites with the ovum?" Yes, you have life in a sense, but you have no blood and no breath of life, two requisities for a living soul. Remember your embryology? The fertilized ovum divides. It divides again and again. After a great number of divisions you have a blastosphere, a dependent growing living mass of tissue without blood and without breath. The human embryo follows practically the same progression of changes many of you have studied in biology and embryology or have seen in time lapse microphotography on the television screen of the changes that occur in the chicken embryo. As development occurs vessels are formed which contain fluid and red cells. A section of the vessels destined to become the heart begins an intrinsic rhythmical pulsation which initiates a circulation even before a heart is formed.

Who would be so naive as to say the embryo is a living soul

when only one red cell is present. Would you say it is a living soul when the heart has not yet been formed yet there is a circulation of blood from the pulsating vessels? Its growth and survival is dependent upon its relationship to the placenta and the mother.

We know that as growth of the embyro continues it grows into what we term the fetus. The fetus continues to develop and at some time during the latter half of pregnancy it becomes large enough to survive outside of the womb of the mother. I think the interruption of the pregnancy sometimes before this is not destructive of a human being.

I realize many will disagree with me, but let me propose several hypothetical cases and see if you are consistent in your thinking and judgments. Many with whom I have talked want one set of criteria if it is their wives or daughters and another set of criteria if it is someone else's wife or daughter.

Suppose for example your wife or daughter were raped. Would you be willing for her to be taken immediately to the hospital and have a uterine dilation and currettage? The common term for this operation is D & C. It is done frequently for diagnosis, for irregular bleeding, for retained placental tissue and for intra-uterine growths. If you would be willing for your raped wife or daughter to have this operation as soon after the attack as possible to prevent a pregnancy from ensuing, would you be willing to have it done at one hour? at two hours? at four hours? at one week? at one month? or at two months? Would you want to wait until she missed a period? Would you be willing for her to have a D & C as soon as the frog pregnancy test is positive Remember after two missed periods the fetus is only a couple of inches long and is still in the stage of development. Survival outside of the uterus is impossible.

It may be a different matter if the pregnancy is a result of a rape. Think, however, about the woman who will develop a true psychosis with suicidal determination who becomes pregnant. Would you sacrifice her pregnancy to salvage her to permit her to raise her other children?

Would you agree to interrupt the pregnancy of the woman who has a constitutional disease such as many of the collagen diseases; for example lupus erythematosis disseminata or scleroderma, which progress so rapidly during a pregnancy that the mother succumbs to her disease before the pregnancy is at term and deliverable?

Would you want a woman to carry to term and deliver a child with the great possibility of it being blind, deformed or mentally deficient if she developed Rubella (german measles) during the fourth to eighth week of pregnancy?

Remember seeing pictures of the armless and legless babies delivered to mothers who took Thalidomide during their first trimester of pregnancy. If your wife or daughter was given Thalidomide or some other known teratogenic drug during her first trimester, would you not agree to a therapeutic abortion or would you want her to carry the pregnancy to term and deliver such a deformed child?

Next, think about the woman who has had three afflicted babies because of an hereditary congenital-condition. If she becomes pregnant again by the same husband, would you require that she carry the pregnancy to term or would you agree to a merciful therapeutic abortion?

How would you advise a couple who comes in with their thirteen- or fourteen-year-old daughter who has missed a period and who has a positive pregnancy test? Would you take the holier than thou attitude that they should have taught her better or they should have watched her closer? Would you let her carry it to term and put it out for adoption? Would you ship her to another city for delivery so that not many would guess what happened to her? You could make immediate discrete secret preparations for an abortion so the girl could return to school and not be ostracized and humiliated for life. I have advised parents and girls both ways. The girls who have had abortions have fared much better. They are not as guilt ridden as those who have given up their babies. They have not had nine months of humilations. They do not have the nightmares because of the reinforced memories of suffering, rejection, anxieties and continual wondering if every baby they see of a certain age could be their baby.

I have seen those who kept their babies, but because of lack of training, lack of job skills and no mate to care for the baby turn to prostitution to keep their baby from going hungry.

I have seen girls keep their babies that have become more

140

and more embittered against them because of the inconvenience of the baby, the expense of the baby and being tied down by the child. They treat the child as unwanted as it is.

How many of the children who are brought to the emergency rooms because of being beaten should not have been delivered to the parents at all. The battered child syndrome is not an uncommon occurrence.

If you agree that just one of these pregnancies should be interrupted, then you and I agree in principle that there is a place for therapeutic abortions. We may not agree on all the indications, but let us not be too critical of those who advise or seek abortions. We may not know all their problems, their health, their mental status, their social status or other factors that are influencing them in their decision.

Study the Scriptures and make up your own mind as to what they teach. Remember it is not a living soul until God breathes into it "the breath of life."

CHAPTER 22

Oral Genital Sex

I TOLD you when we started this series that I would attempt to answer any questions asked provided the questioner signed his or her name.

I have received the following question. "What about oral genital sex?"

I assume the question relates to married couples since we have shown in every lesson that any sexual relationship out of the bonds of marriage is sinful. I think also the question relates to sexual stimulation during the foreplay prior to intercourse. Remember we have read every Scripture that we could find concerning the sex act. We read every Scripture that condemned any sex act. We found no Scripture that condemned a sex act between a man and his wife. Every Scripture that we found that condemned a sex act condemned an act between a man and a woman not his wife, a woman and a man not her husband or between a human and an animal. We found no Scripture regulating how the foreplay or the sexual act should be carried on between a man and his wife.

Alfred Kinsey reported in 1953 that among the married in the United States in his samples fifty-four per cent of the males orally stimulated the female genitalia and forty-nine per cent of females orally stimulated the male genitalia as one pre-coital technique. Admittedly, this technique was not utilized as often as manual stimulation of man and female genitalia, oral and manual stimulation of the female breast, deep kissing and simple kissing.[1] It was, however, utilized by half the couples on occasion. I bring up these statistics not necessarily in defense of this technique, but to let you know of its wide range of use before you categorically condemn it.

I want to ask my audience some questions. Is it right to kiss on the lips? How about deep kissing? Is the kissing of the

------

[1] *Sexual Behavior in the Human Female*, 1953. Alfred C. Kinsey, Wardell P. Pomeroy, Clyde E. Martin and Paul H. Gebhardt, p. 399.

breast alright? Can a man kiss his wife's abdomen? Can a wife enjoy kissing her husband's ear, his arm, his neck, his chest, his abdomen or his thigh? All will answer yes to some of these questions. Some will answer no to others of them. Who is to draw the line and say arbitrarily to kiss some places is fine, but to kiss these other places is wrong. I bring this up, because I have had one of my patients, a member of the church, accuse her husband of being perverted because he wanted to kiss her other than on her mouth. She thought for her husband to want to kiss her breasts was an indication of perversion. I ask again who is to decide where kissing is permissible and where it is not permissible for a man and his wife.

Remember in our lessons on perversions that a perversion was a condition in which men or women had emotional and sexual interest in members of the same sex, in things, in animals and in certain non-marital sexual (to them) stimulating situations.

I think this woman has failed to consider the Scriptures and facts before she made up her mind. I feel that if an act is not condemned specifically and is not condemned by inference then it is up to the individual couple to decide what techniques of pre-coital foreplay in which to engage.

Let me also say that if either partner (man or wife) should have reservations concerning any act, then the other partner should not insist or try to encourage the other to engage or participate in the activity. Remember Romans 14:23 teaches, "For whatsoever is not of faith is sin." I think if a person thinks it is wrong to engage in a certain type of pre-coital foreplay then to participate would be for this person a sin.

For example, if a woman feels it is wrong for her husband to fondle and kiss her breasts, then he should yield to her wishes. However, we quoted seven passages of Scripture in which Solomon made reference to the breasts and the enjoyment derived from his lovers' breasts (Proverbs 5:18-19; Song of Solomon 1:13; 5:4; 7:3; 7:8; 8:10). From these we determined that foreplay with the breasts was not sinful.

We determined that foreplay should be mutually pleasurable, stimulating, enjoyable and not repulsive. If a married partner insists on some act that is not pleasurable, stimulating or enjoyable but rather is repulsive, then instead of enhancing the peak of excitement it will "turn off" or "cool off" the partner.

Attempt to be kind, sympathetic, gentle and understanding in all foreplay. After all the goal in intercourse is to satisfy your partner; if you do this you in turn should be satisfied and gratified.

I think it is most unfortunate that many people harbor guilt feelings because of something they think the Bible teaches which in fact it does not. For example I recall a middle-aged widow who was overwrought with guilt and self-degradation. The reason was that she on occasion had oral genital contacts with her husband many years before. Unfortunately this woman knew little of the teachings of the Bible on any subject. At the time she consulted me she was so emotionally disturbed she was not reachable by teaching. Help was sought from a psychiatrist.

A word of warning—let us follow the teachings and principles of Christ, but let us not condemn where he does not condemn. Let us not feel guilty when we are not guilty.

Conclusion

MY HOPE is that the reader will have a happier and more satisfying life because of this book, that you have become aware that the Bible deals with each of these subjects.

I have attempted to present in a fair non-biased manner the Scriptures that relate to sex. Realizing that many of these subjects have been neglected and avoided and some have even been considered taboo, I have attempted in most instances not only to state what I think the Scriptures teach, but to tell you why I make these interpretations.

My motives in presenting these lessons and preparing this book are the following. God's way is best. His Word is complete and instructs man in every good work. We should know all the Scriptures. Any topic discussed in the Bible is proper subject for discussion in class or from the pulpit. There is a definite need for this type of lessons.

Let these studies be only the beginnings of your investigations. Study your Bible. Digest its teachings. Apply them to your own sexual life. Be strict with your own self in obeying God's commands. Be kind toward others. Remember their temptations may be greater. Remember the sex drive is not the same in every person.